GRADE 4

Polished Spiral Karin Kuhlmann

"Although the creation of fractals is bounded to strict mathematical rules, the results are always very inspiring."— **Karin Kuhlmann**

Implementing Investigations in Grade 4

Investigations

IN NUMBER, DATA, AND SPACE®

Glenview, Illinois • Boston, Massachusetts
Chandler, Arizona • Upper Saddle River, New Jersey

The Investigations Curriculum was developed by TERC, Cambridge, MA.

This material is based on work supported by the National Science Foundation ("NSF") under Grant No. ESI-0095450. Any opinions, findings, and conclusions or recommendations expressed in this material are those of the author(s) and do not necessarily reflect the views of the National Science Foundation.

ISBN-13: 978-0-328-60218-6

ISBN-10: 0-328-60218-3

4 5 6 7 8 9 10 V063 14 13

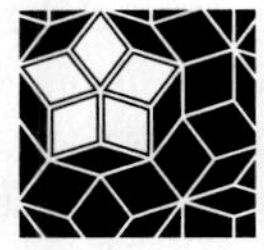

Co-Principal Investigators

Susan Jo Russell

Karen Economopoulos

Authors

Lucy Wittenberg
Director Grades 3–5

Karen Economopoulos
Director Grades K–2

Virginia Bastable
(SummerMath for Teachers, Mt. Holyoke College)

Katie Hickey Bloomfield

Keith Cochran

Darrell Earnest

Arusha Hollister

Nancy Horowitz

Erin Leidl

Megan Murray

Young Oh

Beth W. Perry

Susan Jo Russell

Deborah Schifter
(Education Development Center)

Kathy Sillman

Administrative Staff

Amy Taber
Project Manager

Beth Bergeron

Lorraine Brooks

Emi Fujiwara

Contributing Authors

Denise Baumann

Jennifer DiBrienza

Hollee Freeman

Paula Hooper

Jan Mokros

Stephen Monk
(University of Washington)

Mary Beth O'Connor

Judy Storeygard

Cornelia Tierney

Elizabeth Van Cleef

Carol Wright

Technology

Jim Hammerman

Classroom Field Work

Amy Appell

Rachel E. Davis

Traci Higgins

Julia Thompson

Note: Unless otherwise noted, all contributors listed above were staff of the Education Research Collaborative at TERC during their work on the curriculum. Other affiliations during the time of development are listed.

Collaborating Teachers

This group of dedicated teachers carried out extensive field testing in their classrooms, met regularly to discuss issues of teaching and learning mathematics, provided feedback to staff, welcomed staff into their classrooms to document students' work, and contributed both suggestions and written material that has been incorporated into the curriculum.

Bethany Altchek
Linda Amaral
Kimberly Beauregard
Barbara Bernard
Nancy Buell
Rose Christiansen
Chris Colbath-Hess
Lisette Colon
Kim Cook
Frances Cooper
Kathleen Drew
Rebeka Eston Salemi
Thomas Fisher
Michael Flynn
Holly Ghazey
Susan Gillis
Danielle Harrington
Elaine Herzog
Francine Hiller
Kirsten Lee Howard
Liliana Klass
Leslie Kramer
Melissa Lee Andrichak
Kelley Lee Sadowski
Jennifer Levitan
Mary Lou LoVecchio
Kristen McEnaney
Maura McGrail
Kathe Millett
Florence Molyneaux
Amy Monkiewicz
Elizabeth Monopoli
Carol Murray
Robyn Musser
Christine Norrman
Deborah O'Brien
Timothy O'Connor
Anne Marie O'Reilly
Mark Paige
Margaret Riddle
Karen Schweitzer
Elisabeth Seyferth
Susan Smith
Debra Sorvillo
Shoshanah Starr
Janice Szymaszek
Karen Tobin
JoAnn Trauschke
Ana Vaisenstein
Yvonne Watson
Michelle Woods
Mary Wright

Advisors

Deborah Lowenberg Ball,
University of Michigan

Hyman Bass, Professor of Mathematics and Mathematics Education
University of Michigan

Mary Canner, Principal, Natick Public Schools

Thomas Carpenter, Professor of Curriculum and Instruction,
University of Wisconsin–Madison

Janis Freckmann, Elementary Mathematics Coordinator,
Milwaukee Public Schools

Lynne Godfrey, Mathematics Coach,
Cambridge Public Schools

Ginger Hanlon, Instructional Specialist in Mathematics,
New York City Public Schools

DeAnn Huinker, Director, Center for Mathematics and
Science Education Research, University of Wisconsin–Milwaukee

James Kaput, Professor of Mathematics,
University of Massachusetts–Dartmouth

Kate Kline, Associate Professor, Department of Mathematics
and Statistics, Western Michigan University

Jim Lewis, Professor of Mathematics,
University of Nebraska–Lincoln

William McCallum, Professor of Mathematics,
University of Arizona

Harriet Pollatsek, Professor of Mathematics,
Mt. Holyoke College

Debra Shein-Gerson, Elementary Mathematics Specialist,
Weston Public Schools

Gary Shevell, Assistant Principal,
New York City Public Schools

Liz Sweeney, Elementary Math Department,
Boston Public Schools

Lucy West, Consultant,
Metamorphosis: Teaching Learning Communities, Inc.

This revision of the curriculum was built on the work of the many authors who contributed to the first edition (published between 1994 and 1998). We acknowledge the critical contributions of these authors in developing the content and pedagogy of *Investigations:*

Authors

Joan Akers

Michael T. Battista

Douglas H. Clements

Karen Economopoulos

Marlene Kliman

Jan Mokros

Megan Murray

Ricardo Nemirovsky

Andee Rubin

Susan Jo Russell

Cornelia Tierney

Contributing Authors

Mary Berle-Carman

Rebecca B. Corwin

Rebeka Eston

Claryce Evans

Anne Goodrow

Cliff Konold

Chris Mainhart

Sue McMillen

Jerrie Moffet

Tracy Noble

Kim O'Neil

Mark Ogonowski

Julie Sarama

Amy Shulman Weinberg

Margie Singer

Virginia Woolley

Tracey Wright

Contents

Contents

PART 1

Collaborating with the Authors

Goals and Guiding Principles

Investigations in Number, Data, and Space is a K–5 mathematics curriculum designed to engage students in making sense of mathematical ideas. Six major goals guided the development of this curriculum. The curriculum is designed to

- Support students to make sense of mathematics and learn that they can be mathematical thinkers.
- Focus on computational fluency with whole numbers as a major goal of the elementary grades.
- Provide substantive work in important areas of mathematics—rational numbers, geometry, measurement, data, and early algebra—and connections among them.
- Emphasize reasoning about mathematical ideas.
- Communicate mathematics content and pedagogy to teachers.
- Engage the range of learners in understanding mathematics.

Underlying these goals are three guiding principles that are touchstones for the *Investigations* team as we approach both students and teachers as agents of their own learning:

1. *Students have mathematical ideas.* Students come to school with ideas about numbers, shapes, measurements, patterns, and data. If given the opportunity to learn in an environment that stresses making sense of mathematics, students build on the ideas they already have and learn about new mathematics they have never encountered. They learn mathematical content and develop fluency and skill that is well grounded in meaning. Students learn that they are capable of having mathematical ideas, applying what they know to new situations, and thinking and reasoning about unfamiliar problems.
2. *Teachers are engaged in ongoing learning* about mathematics content, pedagogy, and student learning. The curriculum provides material for professional development, to be used by teachers individually or in groups, that supports teachers' continued learning as they use the curriculum over several years. The *Investigations* curriculum materials are designed as much to be a dialogue with teachers as to be a core of content for students.
3. *Teachers collaborate with the students and curriculum materials* to create the curriculum as enacted in the classroom. The only way for a good curriculum to be used well is for teachers to be active participants in implementing it. Teachers use the curriculum to maintain a clear, focused, and coherent agenda for mathematics teaching. At the same time, they observe and listen carefully to students, try to understand how they are thinking, and make teaching decisions based on these observations.

The Teacher-Student-Curriculum Partnership

Mathematics teaching and learning at its best is a collaboration among teachers, students, and the curriculum. Both the teacher and the curriculum contribute to this partnership in important ways. The curriculum materials provide a coherent, carefully sequenced core of mathematics content for students and supportive professional development material for teachers. Teachers are active partners in learning the curriculum well, understanding how each mathematical focus is developed, and implementing the curriculum in a way that accommodates the needs of their particular students.

The *Investigations* curriculum was field-tested in many different classrooms, representing a range of students and teachers, over several years. Thousands of hours of classroom observation, documentation, analysis of student work, and meetings with teachers were involved. Activities and the way they are presented to students were revised again and again.

Each time a curriculum unit was tested in a classroom, no matter how many times it had been tried and revised before, there was always more to discover about how students learn and how activities can be revised and modified to support them. This process, we have come to believe, can be endless. Just as you, a classroom teacher, learn more about students' learning each year, so do those of us who develop the curriculum. At some point we decide that, considering all the evidence, the curriculum has been sufficiently tested and works well for a wide range of students.

This lengthy and detailed process has resulted in a coherent core curriculum that is based on the real needs of real students and teachers. The process has also provided ample evidence that the collaboration of the teacher is essential. Only the teacher can understand and support the particular learning needs of a particular class of students in a particular school year. Only the teacher is present every day in the classroom, observing students' work, listening to their discourse, and developing an understanding of their mathematical ideas by analyzing what they say and do. In mathematics, as in any subject, only the teacher can continually assess students' strengths and needs and think through how best to accommodate differences to involve all students in substantive and challenging work.

How *Investigations* Supports the Teacher's Role

Modifying the curriculum and making it work in your classroom requires knowing the curriculum well. It means taking the time to understand the mathematics focus of each lesson and how the mathematical ideas build over many lessons. Learning the curriculum well means holding back the urge to change activities because you think they are too easy or too difficult for your students before you have tried them and actually seen your students' work. Keep in mind that the way ideas are developed and sequenced has been researched and tested in multiple classrooms, and many suggestions for accommodations are already built into the curriculum. Teachers tell us that they generally follow the curriculum as it is written the first year, and that they learn a great deal when activities that they thought would not work with their students turn out to be crucial to student learning.

You are an active partner in this teacher-student-curriculum partnership, and the curriculum must support your complex job by providing information about mathematics content and student learning. From the beginning, our intention in developing *Investigations* has been to create a professional development tool for teachers—a tool that provides opportunities for learning about mathematics content, how students learn, and effective pedagogy. Our design focuses as much on the teacher as learner as on the student as learner.

Two sections at the beginning of each curriculum unit, Mathematics in This Unit and Assessment in This Unit, provide an overview of the mathematics content, Math Focus Points, and benchmarks for student learning. The Math Focus Points for each session and the assessment benchmarks tell the mathematical story line of each curriculum unit so that you can productively guide students' work. Math Focus Points make explicit the purposes of the activities in each session and help you make choices about how to guide discussions. The assessment benchmarks for each curriculum unit are an aid in determining priorities and interpreting students' work.

The "teacher talk" printed in blue in each session is also an aid for focusing an activity and choosing questions to ask. It is not a script for how to address your students; it is a guide based on classroom experience with different ways of talking about mathematical ideas, introducing activities, and asking effective questions.

Teacher Notes collected at the end of each curriculum unit focus on key mathematical ideas and how students learn them. Because having students reason about, articulate, and justify their ideas is such a central part of the curriculum,

Dialogue Boxes provide examples of student discussion and teachers' efforts to focus this discussion. Additionally, examples of what students might say in class appear within the session descriptions.

To further support your work with the curriculum, this *Implementing Investigations in Grade 4* book provides an overview of the math content for the entire year (Part 3), a set of Teacher Notes that applies to the curriculum as a whole (Part 6), and a set of classroom cases written by teachers that provides examples of how they work with the range of learners in their classrooms (Part 7).

Teachers who use the *Investigations* curriculum over several years find that, as they teach a curriculum unit more than once, they gradually read more and more of the supporting material and incorporate it into their work with students. Teachers also use features such as the Teacher Notes and Dialogue Boxes as part of grade-level study groups or within other professional development structures. The better you know the curriculum and your students, the more you can internalize the mathematics focus and sequence and the better decisions you can make to support your students' learning.

Components of the Program

Curriculum Units

The curriculum at each grade level is organized into nine units (seven for kindergarten). These curriculum units are your teaching guides for the program. The unit organization is further described in the next section, "Using the Curriculum Units."

Each curriculum unit in Grade 4 offers from 3 to 5 weeks of work and focuses on the area of mathematics identified in the unit's subtitle.

This pacing is based on a school year that starts in early September, ends in late June, and has vacation weeks in February and April. The pacing will vary according to school calendars but may also vary depending on the needs of students, the school's years of experience with this curriculum, and other local factors.

Grade 4 Curriculum Units

Unit	Title	Number of Sessions	Suggested Pacing
1	**Factors, Multiples, and Arrays** Multiplication and Division 1	**14**	**September**
2	**Describing the Shape of the Data** Data Analysis and Probability	**17**	**September–October**
3	**Multiple Towers and Division Stories** Multiplication and Division 2	**20**	**October–November**
4	**Size, Shape, and Symmetry** 2-D Geometry and Measurement	**20**	**December**
5	**Landmarks and Large Numbers** Addition, Subtraction, and the Number System	**24**	**January–early February**
6	**Fraction Cards and Decimal Squares** Fractions and Decimals	**20**	**February–March**
7	**Moving Between Solids and Silhouettes** 3-D Geometry and Measurement	**14**	**April**
8	**How Many Packages? How Many Groups?** Multiplication and Division 3	**16**	**May**
9	**Penny Jars and Plant Growth** Patterns, Functions, and Change	**15**	**June**

The curriculum units are designed for use in the sequence shown. Each succeeding unit builds on the previous unit, both within and across strands. For example, the three units that focus on multiplication (Units 1, 3, and 8) develop a sequence of ideas across the three units. Across strands, both Unit 7 (3-D Geometry and Measurement) and Unit 9 (Patterns, Functions, and Change) build on the ideas about multiplication but use new contexts.

Resource Masters and Transparencies

Each Resource Masters and Transparencies CD contains the reproducible materials needed for classroom instruction. The use of all these materials for particular Investigations is specified in the curriculum units.

Investigations Software

LogoPaths Software for Grade 4 provides an environment in which students investigate movement along paths, length, perimeter, angle, and the characteristics of a variety of shapes. This software is provided as a disk to be used with Unit 4, *Size, Shape, and Symmetry,* and is also available through the Pearson website.

Investigations for the Interactive Whiteboard

Each grade has whole-class instructional support that enhances the session's content as well as the daily Ten-Minute Math activity.

Differentiation and Intervention Handbook

Differentiation activities are included for each Investigation along with a quiz that can be used after an Investigation is completed.

Student Activity Book

A booklet accompanying each curriculum unit contains the consumable pages for student work, including in-class work, game recording sheets, and all pages for daily practice and for homework. The *Student Activity Book* is also available as a single volume, with all the curriculum units in one book.

Student Math Handbook

A single handbook for each grade level in Grades 1–5 offers a valuable reference to the math words and ideas introduced in the curriculum units, as well as instruction pages for playing all the games. This book is designed to be used flexibly: as a resource for students during class work, as a book students can take home for reference while doing homework and playing math games with their families, and/or as a reference for families to better understand the work their children are doing in class.

Manipulatives Kit

A kit of materials is coordinated with the activities and games at each grade level. The Grade 4 kit includes class sets of the following items:

- Connecting cubes
- Wooden geometric solids
- Power Polygons™
- Color tiles
- Blank cubes and labels, for making number cubes
- Coin sets (pennies, nickels, dimes, quarters, half dollars, dollars)
- Metersticks/yardsticks
- Rulers
- Geoboards
- Class number line
- Overhead tools: transparent counters and color tiles

Cards in Card Kit

Manufactured cards are used with some of the activities and games at each grade level. The cards for Grade 4 are as follows:

Digit Cards
Grade 4 Array Cards
Grade 4 Decimal Cards
Multiple Cards

Implementing *Investigations* in Grade 4

At each grade level, this guide to implementing *Investigations* includes an overview of the curriculum; suggestions for using the curriculum units in your classroom; a closer look at the mathematics content of that particular grade, including lists of the Math Focus Points for each curriculum unit; program-wide Teacher Notes that explain some key ideas underlying the curriculum; and a set of case studies about working with a range of learners that can be used for professional development.

The Curriculum Units

The curriculum unit is your main teaching tool. It is your blueprint for the sequence and purpose of the daily lessons; it also contains guidelines for assessment, suggestions for differentiating instruction, and professional development materials to support your teaching.

Structure of a Curriculum Unit

Each curriculum unit is divided into Investigations. An Investigation focuses on a set of related mathematical ideas, coordinating students' work in hands-on activities, written activities, and class discussions over a period of several days.

Investigations are divided into one-hour *sessions,* or lessons. Sessions include the following features:

- *Math Focus Points:* This list of what students will be doing mathematically highlights the goals of each session.
- *Activities:* A session contains from one to three activities, organized as work for the whole class, pairs, small groups, or individuals.
- *Discussion:* Many sessions include whole-class time during which students compare methods and results and share conclusions. A subset of the session's Math Focus Points helps you guide each discussion.
- *Math Workshop:* In some sessions, students work in a Math Workshop format. Individually, in pairs, or in small groups, they choose from and cycle through a set of related activities. This setup is further discussed in a later section, "All About Math Workshop" (pages 12–13).
- *Assessment:* Students are assessed through both written activities and observations; see "Assessment in This Unit" for further information.
- *Session Follow-Up:* Homework is provided for 3–4 days per week at Grade 4. In addition, each session includes a page for Daily Practice. These pages offer either ongoing review of materials from previous curriculum units or directed practice of content in the current curriculum unit. They can be used either for additional homework or for in-class practice. Relevant pages in the *Student Math Handbook* are also referenced here.

Your Math Day

The *Investigations* curriculum assumes that you spend 1 hour of each classroom day on mathematics, in addition to conducting brief Ten-Minute Math activities (further described later in this section and in Part 4 of this book). A chart called Today's Plan appears at the beginning of each session, laying out the suggested pacing for the activities in that 1-hour session. While you may need to adapt this structure to your particular classroom needs, be aware that it is important to move through all the activities because they are carefully designed to offer continued work on the key mathematical ideas. It is also essential that you allow time for class discussions, where students have an opportunity to articulate their own ideas, compare solutions, and consolidate understanding. See Teacher Note: Discussing Mathematical Ideas, on pages 57–59, for further information on the importance of these class discussions.

Differentiated Instruction

Within the sessions, you will regularly see a feature titled "Differentiation: Supporting the Range of Learners." This feature offers ideas for intervention or extensions related to the particular work of that session. Ideas for helping English Language Learners are offered at the beginning of the curriculum unit and where applicable in the sessions. In addition, Part 7 of this book, "Working with the Range of Learners: Classroom Cases," presents situations from actual *Investigations* classrooms and invites you to consider how these case studies can inform your own teaching practice.

Ten-Minute Math

These brief activities, described in a box below Today's Plan for each session, require 10–15 minutes of additional daily work outside of math time. These activities, an important part of the *Investigations* curriculum, offer ongoing skill building, practice, and review that support the regular math work; they also reinforce the work students have done in previous units and help students increase their repertoire of strategies for mental calculation and problem solving. Part 4 of this book, "Ten-Minute Math," provides detailed explanations of the activities to plan for Grade 4.

Assessment in This Unit

Opportunities for assessment are carefully woven throughout the curriculum units. A section at the beginning of each curriculum unit identifies the benchmarks students will be expected to meet and specifies key activities you can observe, as well as the particular assessment activities where students will produce written work for your review. The final session in each curriculum unit is devoted to the End-of-Unit Assessment. Each written assessment in the curriculum unit is accompanied by a Teacher Note that provides examples of student work and guidelines that help you assess whether your students are meeting the benchmarks. For observed assessments, an assessment checklist is provided; here you can record notes about what students understand as you observe them engaged in the session's activities.

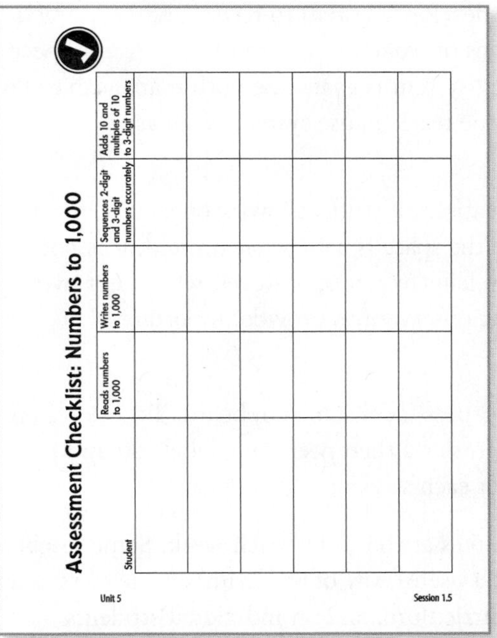

Assessment Checklist: Numbers to 1,000

Student	Reads numbers to 1,000	Writes numbers to 1,000	Sequences 2-digit and 3-digit numbers accurately	Adds 10 and multiples of 10 to 3-digit numbers

Unit 5 Session 1.5

▲ An example of an Assessment Checklist

"Ongoing Assessment: Observing Students at Work" is a regular feature of the sessions. It identifies the particular math focus and lists questions for you to consider as you observe your students solving problems, playing math games, and working on activities. Teacher observations are an important part of ongoing assessment. Although individual observations may be little more than snapshots of a student's experience with a single activity, when considered together over time, they can provide an informative and detailed picture. These observations can be useful in documenting and assessing a student's growth and offer important sources of information when preparing for family conferences or writing student reports.

You may want to develop a system to record and keep track of your observations of students. The most important aspect of a record-keeping system is that it be both manageable and useful for you. Some teachers use systems such as the following:

- Jot down observations of students' work on a class list of names. Because the space is somewhat limited, it is not possible to write lengthy notes; however, when kept over time, these short observations provide important information.
- Place stick-on address labels on a clipboard. Take notes on individual students and then peel these labels off and put them in a file for each student.
- Jot down brief notes at the end of each week. Some teachers find that this is a useful way of reflecting on the class as a whole, on the curriculum, and on individual students. Planning for the next week's activities can benefit from these weekly reflections.

Observation checklists, student work on written assessments, and other examples of students' written work can be collected in a portfolio. Suggestions for particular work that might be saved in a portfolio are listed at the beginning of each curriculum unit, under "Assessment in This Unit."

Professional Development

One guiding principle of the *Investigations* curriculum is to provide support that helps teachers improve their own understanding of the mathematics that they are teaching and the learning that they observe in their students. To this end, the following materials are included in the curriculum for teachers' professional development:

- *Mathematics in This Unit:* An essay at the beginning of each curriculum unit explains in detail the Mathematical Emphases of the unit, the Math Focus Points related to each area of emphasis, and the work students will be doing in each area.
- *Algebra Connections in This Unit:* This essay, appearing in each of the number and operations units and in the patterns, functions, and change units, explains how the activities and ideas of the curriculum unit are laying a foundation for students' later work with algebra.
- *Math Notes, Teaching Notes, and Algebra Notes:* Found in the margins of the sessions, these brief notes provide information about mathematics content or student thinking, as well as teaching tips to help teachers better understand the work of that session.
- *Teacher Notes:* These essays, collected at the end of each curriculum unit, provide further practical information about the mathematics content and how students learn it. Many of the notes were written in response to questions from teachers or to discuss important issues that arose in field-test classrooms. They offer teachers help with thinking about mathematical ideas that may be unfamiliar to them; they also provide guidance for observing and assessing students' work.
- *Dialogue Boxes:* Also at the end of each curriculum unit are Dialogue Boxes that reflect classroom scenarios related to the activities of the unit. Since these Dialogue Boxes are based on actual teacher-student interactions, you learn how students typically express their mathematical ideas, what issues and confusions arise in their thinking, and how some teachers have chosen to guide particular class discussions.

Working with Families

Families are important partners with schools in the process of teaching mathematics. Because the teaching of mathematics has been evolving, many families may be unfamiliar with the approaches taken by the *Investigations* curriculum. For this reason, a number of Family Letters are provided. In Grade 4, these letters include the following:

- The first Family Letter in each curriculum unit, About the Mathematics in This Unit, introduces families to the mathematics that their children will be doing and to the benchmarks for that unit.
- A second letter in each curriculum unit, Related Activities to Try at Home, is sent home a few days after the first. It suggests related activities that families can do together and children's books that support students' work in mathematics.
- An additional letter provided in the first curriculum unit of the year, About Mathematics Homework, gives suggestions for helping students with their homework by establishing a regular time for homework, setting up a good working environment, and asking productive questions

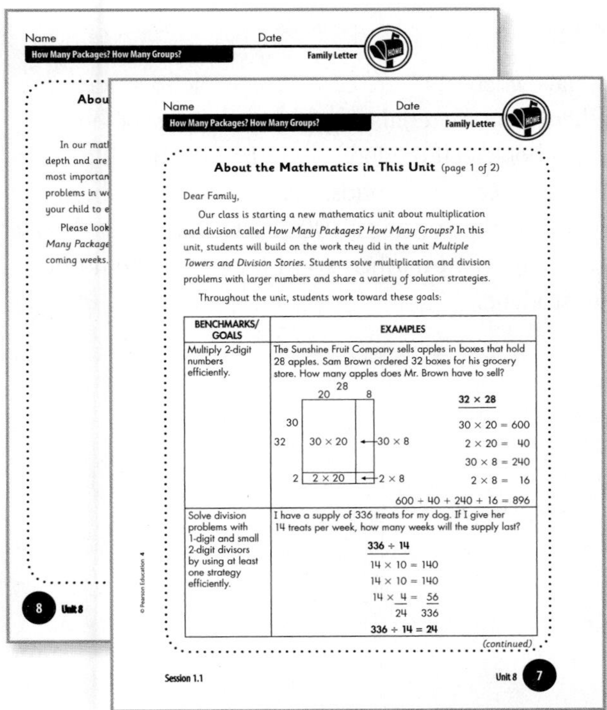
Name Date

How Many Packages? How Many Groups? Family Letter

About the Mathematics in This Unit (page 1 of 2)

Dear Family,

Our class is starting a new mathematics unit about multiplication and division called *How Many Packages? How Many Groups?* In this unit, students will build on the work they did in the unit *Multiple Towers and Division Stories.* Students solve multiplication and division problems with larger numbers and share a variety of solution strategies.

Throughout the unit, students work toward these goals:

BENCHMARKS/ GOALS	EXAMPLES
Multiply 2-digit numbers efficiently.	The Sunshine Fruit Company sells apples in boxes that hold 28 apples. Sam Brown ordered 32 boxes for his grocery store. How many apples does Mr. Brown have to sell? **32 × 28** 30 × 20 = 600 2 × 20 = 40 30 × 8 = 240 2 × 8 = 16 600 + 40 + 240 + 16 = 896
Solve division problems with 1-digit and small 2-digit divisors by using at least one strategy efficiently.	I have a supply of 336 treats for my dog. If I give her 14 treats per week, how many weeks will the supply last? **336 ÷ 14** 14 × 10 = 140 14 × 10 = 140 14 × 4 = 56 24 336 **336 ÷ 14 = 24**

(continued)

Session 1.1 Unit 8 7

▲ An example of a Family Letter

- Particular to Grade 4, one more Family Letter focuses on the ways students are learning the multiplication combinations (facts) and how parents can support this work at home. The letter on Practicing Multiplication Combinations is provided with Unit 1, *Factors, Multiples, and Arrays.*

The *Student Math Handbook* is another valuable tool for working with families. The Math Words and Ideas section of this book provides an overview of the year's mathematics work, a closer look at the ideas and the kinds of problems students encounter, examples of student solutions, and questions that families and students can talk about together. The handbook also contains game directions for use at school or at home.

Setting Up the *Investigations* Classroom

As you begin using the *Investigations* curriculum, you may find yourself making decisions about how to set up the tables and chairs in your classroom and where to keep your materials. Students will at various times need to work individually, in pairs or small groups, and as a whole class. When working in pairs or small groups, they need to be able to see one another's work and listen to one another's ideas. Bringing students together for whole-group discussion is also a regular feature of the curriculum, and during these discussions it is important that students can easily see and hear one another. Ways of making this work are further discussed in the Teacher Note: Discussing Mathematical Ideas, on pages 57–59. You must also find ways to make materials and games easily accessible and consider how to organize the room for Math Workshops.

Materials as Tools for Learning

In an active mathematics classroom, certain basic materials should be available at all times: connecting cubes, pencils, blank paper, graph paper, calculators, things to count with, and measuring tools. Some activities in the curriculum require glue sticks and scissors or tape. Stick-on notes and large paper for posters are also useful materials.

So students can independently get what they need at any time, they should know where these materials are kept, how they are stored, and how they need to be returned to the storage area. For example, connecting cubes are best stored in towers of 10 and should be replaced in these towers when an activity is completed.

Rationale

Tools and materials are used throughout the *Investigations* curriculum. Students of all ages benefit from being able to use materials to model problems and explain their thinking.

It is important to encourage all students to use tools and materials, such as geometric solids, connecting cubes, rulers, and coin sets. If materials are used only when someone is having difficulty, students may get the mistaken idea that using materials is a less sophisticated and less valued way of solving a problem. Encourage students to talk about how they used certain materials. They should see how different people, including the teacher, use a variety of materials in solving the same problem.

The more available materials are, the more likely students are to use them. Having materials available means that they are readily accessible to students and that students are allowed to make decisions about which tools to use and when to use them. In much the same way as you choose the best tool to use for certain projects or tasks, students should be encouraged to think about which material best meets their needs.

Using materials in the classroom may be a new experience for many students and teachers. Before introducing new materials, think about how you want students to use and care for them, including how they will be stored.

Introducing a New Material

Students need time to explore a new material before using it in structured activities. By freely exploring with new materials, students will discover many of the important characteristics of the new material and will gain some understanding of when it might make sense to use it. Although some free exploration should be done during regular math time, many teachers make materials such as Power Polygons and geometric solids available to students during free time or before or after school.

Plan for how materials will be cleaned up at the end of each class. Most teachers find that stopping 5 minutes before the end of class gives students time to clean up materials, organize and turn in their work, and double-check the floor for any stray materials.

Storing Materials

Store materials where they are easily accessible to students. Many teachers store materials in plastic tubs or shoe boxes arranged on a bookshelf or along a windowsill. In addition to Power Polygons, geometric solids, and connecting cubes, items such as calculators, coins, 100 charts, and paper (blank and grid) are important mathematical tools that should be available to students.

Games in the *Investigations* Curriculum

The games included in this curriculum are a central part of the mathematics in each curriculum unit, not just an enrichment activity. Games are used to develop concepts and to practice skills, such as learning to sort and classify polygons, finding combinations that make 1,000, or sequencing fractions. The rationale for using games is as follows:

- Games provide engaging opportunities for students to deepen their understanding of the number system and operations and to practice computation.
- Playing games encourages strategic mathematical thinking as students find an optimal way (rather than just any way) of "winning" the game.
- Games provide repeated practice without requiring the teacher to provide new problems.
- While students are playing the games, the teacher is free to observe students or to work with individuals or small groups.

Before introducing a game to students, it is important that you play the game for yourself to learn the mathematical ideas that students encounter as they play the game. For some games, variations are offered. Before using these variations, or any others you might think of, consider how changing the rules of the game changes the mathematical ideas with which students are working.

Games are often played frequently throughout a curriculum unit. Once games have been introduced, consider leaving them out throughout the year for students to play. It is expected that students will play a game many times as they develop fluency with numbers, computation, and geometry.

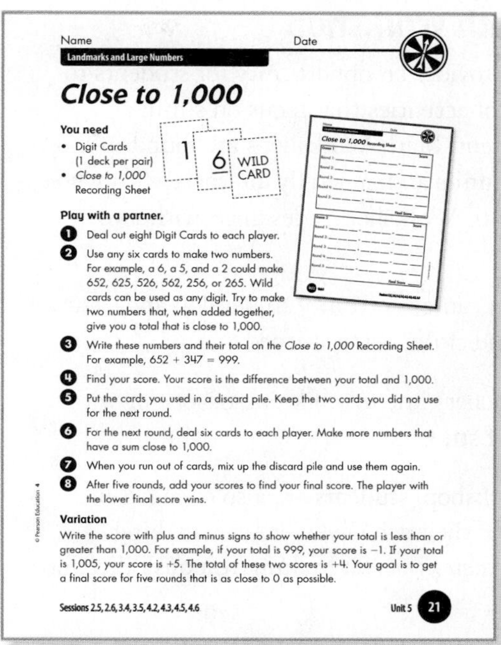

Name Date

Landmarks and Large Numbers

Close to 1,000

You need

- Digit Cards (1 deck per pair)
- *Close to 1,000* Recording Sheet

Play with a partner.

1. Deal out eight Digit Cards to each player.
2. Use any six cards to make two numbers. For example, a 6, a 5, and a 2 could make 652, 625, 526, 562, 256, or 265. Wild cards can be used as any digit. Try to make two numbers that, when added together, give you a total that is close to 1,000.
3. Write these numbers and their total on the *Close to 1,000* Recording Sheet. For example, 652 + 347 = 999.
4. Find your score. Your score is the difference between your total and 1,000.
5. Put the cards you used in a discard pile. Keep the two cards you did not use for the next round.
6. For the next round, deal six cards to each player. Make more numbers that have a sum close to 1,000.
7. When you run out of cards, mix up the discard pile and use them again.
8. After five rounds, add your scores to find your final score. The player with the lower final score wins.

Variation

Write the score with plus and minus signs to show whether your total is less than or greater than 1,000. For example, if your total is 999, your score is −1. If your total is 1,005, your score is +5. The total of these two scores is +4. Your goal is to get a final score for five rounds that is as close to 0 as possible.

Sessions 2.5, 2.6, 3.4, 3.5, 4.2, 4.3, 4.5, 4.6 Unit 5 21

▲ An example of game instructions

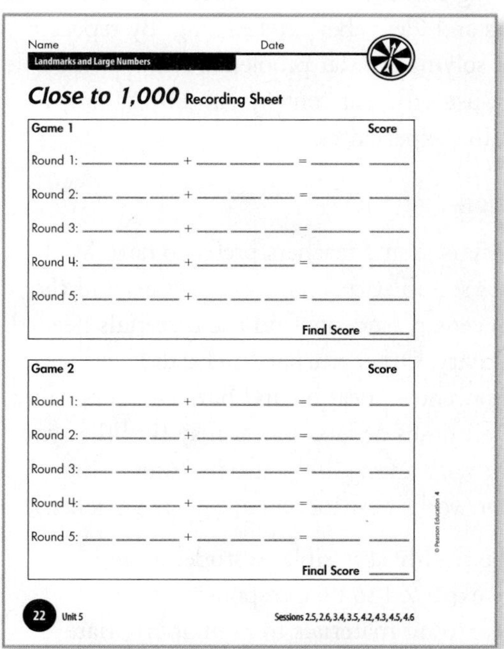

Name Date

Landmarks and Large Numbers

Close to 1,000 Recording Sheet

Game 1	Score
Round 1: ___ ___ ___ + ___ ___ ___ = ______	______
Round 2: ___ ___ ___ + ___ ___ ___ = ______	______
Round 3: ___ ___ ___ + ___ ___ ___ = ______	______
Round 4: ___ ___ ___ + ___ ___ ___ = ______	______
Round 5: ___ ___ ___ + ___ ___ ___ = ______	______
Final Score	______

Game 2	Score
Round 1: ___ ___ ___ + ___ ___ ___ = ______	______
Round 2: ___ ___ ___ + ___ ___ ___ = ______	______
Round 3: ___ ___ ___ + ___ ___ ___ = ______	______
Round 4: ___ ___ ___ + ___ ___ ___ = ______	______
Round 5: ___ ___ ___ + ___ ___ ___ = ______	______
Final Score	______

22 Unit 5 Sessions 2.5, 2.6, 3.4, 3.5, 4.2, 4.3, 4.5, 4.6

▲ An example of a game recording sheet

All About Math Workshop

Math Workshop provides an opportunity for students to work on a variety of activities that focus on similar mathematical content. Math Workshops are found in most of the curriculum units and generally alternate with whole-class activities. Math Workshop is designed with two purposes in mind:

1. To give students an opportunity to develop and practice the concepts and skills being learned

2. To give the teacher time to work one-on-one or with small groups of students

During Math Workshop, students are also engaged in other key aspects of their school experience: making choices, planning their time, and taking responsibility for their own learning.

The activities in Math Workshop are not sequential; as students move among them, they continually revisit the important concepts and ideas they are learning. By repeatedly playing a game, or solving similar problems, students are able to refine strategies, use different contexts, and bring new knowledge to familiar experiences.

Setting Up Math Workshop

Organizing Materials Some teachers prefer to have Math Workshop activities set up at centers or stations around the classroom. At each center, students find the materials needed to complete the activity. Other teachers prefer to have materials stored in a central location and have students bring the materials to their desks or tables. You may find that you need to experiment with a few different structures before finding a setup that works best for you and your students.

Materials should be readily accessible to students, and students should be expected to take responsibility for cleaning up and returning materials to their appropriate storage locations. Giving students a "5 minutes until cleanup" warning before the end of an activity session allows them to finish what they are working on and prepare for the upcoming transition, which is often to a class discussion.

Organizing the Students Each Math Workshop generally includes three to five activities that students do over several class sessions. Support students in organizing their time to complete the activities. Initially you may need to help students plan what they do and in what order, but as the year goes on, students should learn to make their choices, get their materials, engage with an activity for enough time to benefit from it, and then switch activities, without your help.

Often when a new activity is introduced, many students want to do it first. Assure them that they will be able to work on each activity. Some students may want to return to the same activity over and over again, such as a game, without trying other activities. Make sure these students do a different activity first, and then choose the favorite activity as a second choice. Other students may need to be encouraged to use their time efficiently to complete all activities. You may want to limit the number of students who work on a Math Workshop activity at one time. In some cases, the quantity of materials available limits the number of students who can do an activity at any one time. In others, limiting the number of students at one activity gives them the opportunity to work in smaller groups and requires students to make choices among activities.

We do not recommend that you organize students into groups and have each group at each activity for a set amount of time. While this method ensures that each student engages in each activity, it does not provide the flexibility and differentiation needed in the classroom. One student may have accomplished a task and need to move to a different activity, while another may be engaged in good mathematical work at a particular activity for a longer time. For the same reason, we also do not recommend that you conduct Math Workshop activities as whole class activities, one after the other.

The Role of the Student

Establish clear guidelines when you introduce Math Workshop activities. Discuss students' responsibilities:

- Work on every activity at least once.
- Be productively engaged during Math Workshop.
- Ask questions of other students when you don't understand or feel stuck. (Some teachers establish the rule, "Ask two other students before me," which requires students to check with two peers before coming to the teacher for help.)

Students should also determine a method to keep track of their work. Some teachers list the choices for sessions on a chart, the board, or an overhead projector to help students keep track of what they need to do. As students finish an activity, they write it on a list and place any work they have done in their folders.

The Role of the Teacher

Establishing the Routine You will probably find that much of your time during the initial Math Workshops is spent circulating around the classroom helping students get settled into activities and monitoring the overall management of the classroom. Once routines are familiar and well established, students will become more independent and responsible for their work during Math Workshop. This will allow you to spend more concentrated periods of time observing the class as a whole or working with individuals and small groups.

Making Expectations Explicit The amount of work that students are expected to complete will vary from classroom to classroom. Some activities include extensions and additional problems for students who need further practice or extra challenge. Suggestions are also made in the Math Workshop activities and the "Supporting the Range of Learners" sections in the Math Workshop sessions. As students begin each Math Workshop, make certain students know which activities they are expected to complete.

Individual and Small Group Work Math Workshop allows teachers to observe and listen to students while they work. At times, you may want to meet with individual students, pairs, or small groups who might need help (or additional challenges). You may also want to focus on particular students in order to get a better sense of their math understanding. Recording your observations of students will help you keep track of how they are interacting with materials and solving problems.

Sometimes one of the Math Workshop activities is a formal observed assessment. This type of assessment provides an opportunity to assess students as they work on a set of problems or play a game. You can record your observations on the assessment checklist that is provided in the Resources Binder.

Number and Operations: Whole Numbers

Multiplication and Division

In Grade 4, three of the four curriculum units on number and operations with whole numbers focus on multiplication and division. This major component of students' work centers on reasoning about numbers and their factors and multiples; using models, representations, and story contexts to help them visualize and solve multiplication and division problems; and understanding the relationship between multiplication and division.

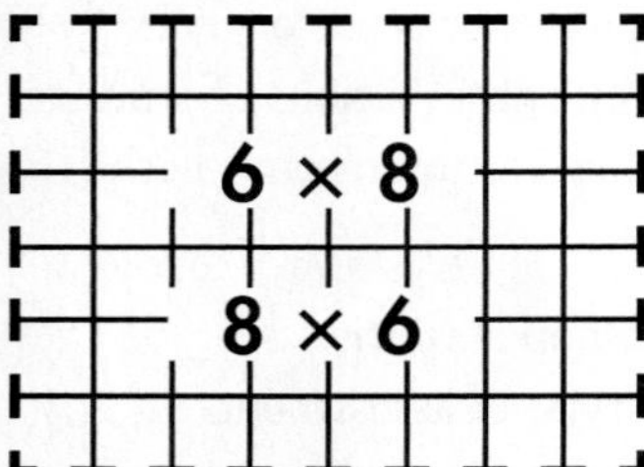

Combinations We're Working On	Start With
6 × 8	5 × 8 (and add one more 8) 3 × 8 (and double it) 6 × 4 (and double it)

Students learn the multiplication combinations (facts) to 12 × 12 so that they can use these fluently to solve both multiplication and division problems. They develop strategies for solving multiplication and division problems based on looking at the problem as a whole, thinking about the relationships of the numbers in the problem, and choosing an approach they can carry out easily and accurately, often breaking the numbers apart or changing the numbers in some way. Visualizing how multiplication works is critical in applying the distributive property to solve problems and in keeping track of the various parts of a problem. Learning to multiply by multiples of 10 is also a key component of this work.

Examples of Multiplication Strategies

Breaking numbers apart by addition

$48 \times 42 =$

$40 \times 40 = 1{,}600$

$40 \times 2 = 80$

$8 \times 40 = 320$

$8 \times 2 = 16$

$1{,}600 + 80 + 320 + 16 = 2{,}016$

$48 \times 42 =$

$48 \times 40 = 1{,}920$

$48 \times 2 = 96$

$1{,}920 + 96 = 2{,}016$

Changing one number to create an easier problem

$48 \times 42 =$

$50 \times 42 = 2{,}100 \left(\frac{1}{2} \text{ of } 100 \times 42\right)$

$2 \times 42 = 84$

$2{,}100 - 84 = 2{,}016$

Students interpret and solve division problems, both in story contexts and numerical contexts. They work with both grouping and sharing situations and consider how to make sense of a remainder within the context of a problem. They use the inverse relationship between multiplication and division to solve division problems, including those related to the multiplication combinations to 12 × 12 (the division "facts"), and problems in which 3-digit numbers are divided by 1-digit and small 2-digit divisors.

Derek bought a book with 144 pages. If he reads 8 pages each day, how many days will it take him to finish the book?

The Algebra Connections pages in the three curriculum units that focus on multiplication and division (Units 1, 3, and 8) show how students are applying the commutative and distributive properties of multiplication, as well as the inverse relationship between multiplication and division, as they solve problems. These pages also highlight particular generalizations about multiplication that students work on in Grade 4: If a number is a factor of a second number, are all the factors of the first number also factors of the second number? If one factor in a multiplication expression is halved and another factor is doubled, what is the effect on the product?

Mathematical Emphases

Whole Number Operations

- Understanding and working with an array model of multiplication
- Reasoning about numbers and their factors
- Understanding and using the relationship between multiplication and division to solve division problems
- Understanding division as making groups of the divisor

Computational Fluency

- Fluency with the multiplication combinations to 12×12
- Solving multiplication problems with 2-digit numbers

Benchmarks (compiled from Units 1, 3, and 8)

- Use known multiplication combinations to find the product of any multiplication combination to 12×12.
- Use arrays, pictures or models of groups, and story contexts to represent multiplication situations.
- Find the factors of 2-digit numbers.
- Multiply 2-digit numbers by 1-digit and small 2-digit numbers (e.g., 12, 15, 20), using strategies that involve breaking the numbers apart.
- Solve division problems (2- and small 3-digit numbers divided by 1-digit numbers), including some that result in a remainder.
- Use story problems, pictures, or concrete models to represent division situations.
- Multiply by 10 and multiples of 10.
- Demonstrate fluency with multiplication combinations to 12×12.
- Multiply 2-digit numbers efficiently.
- Solve division problems with 1- and small 2-digit divisors by using at least one strategy efficiently.

Addition, Subtraction, and the Number System

In Grade 4, students extend their knowledge of the base-ten number system, working with numbers up to 10,000. Their work focuses on understanding the structure of 10,000 and how numbers are related within that structure, recognizing the place value of digits in large numbers, and using place value to determine the magnitude of numbers.

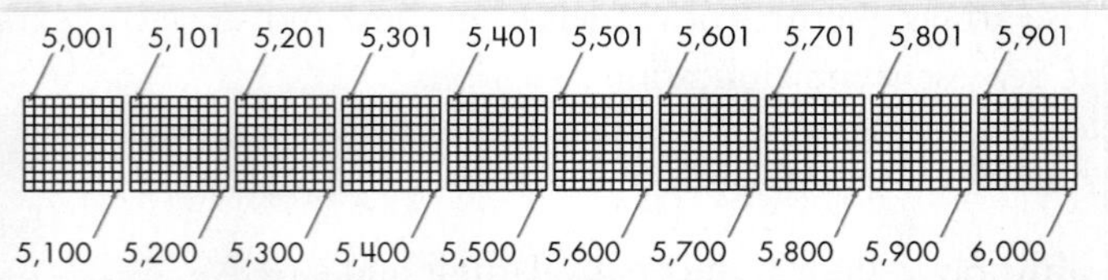

By discussing, refining, and comparing their strategies for adding and subtracting 3- and 4-digit numbers, including studying the U.S. algorithm for addition, students continue to expand their understanding of addition and subtraction. Their strategies should involve good mental arithmetic, estimation, clear and concise notation, and a sound understanding of number relationships. By identifying and naming the addition and subtraction strategies that they are using, students are adding to the repertoire of strategies they can use for flexible and fluent computation. Further, they consider how and why certain methods work. For example, some students change one or both numbers in an addition or subtraction expression to create an easier problem; then they compensate as needed for that change. In this unit, students study *why* certain addition expressions are equivalent (e.g., $457 + 198 = 455 + 200$) and *how* certain expressions in subtraction are related (e.g., $782 - 590$ and $782 - 600$).

$782 - 590 =$ ______

$782 - 600 = 182$

$182 + 10 = 192$

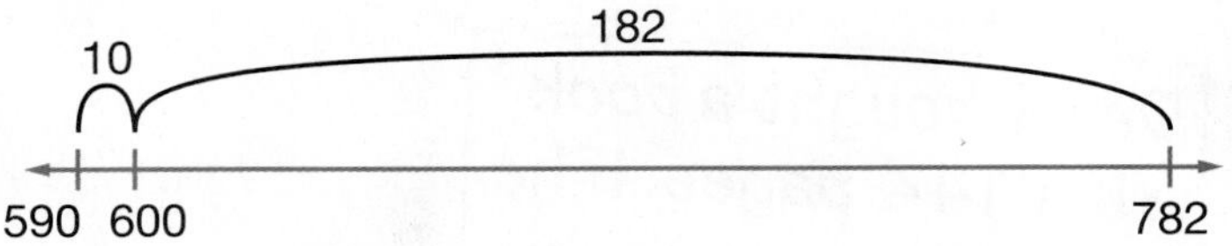

To help them make good decisions about strategies for subtraction and continue to develop their understanding of how subtraction operates, students use visual representations, such as number lines and 100 charts, and story contexts that include several types of subtraction situations—removal (or "take away"), comparison, and missing parts. Students focus particularly on missing part problems in the context of distance:

> On a trip of 631 miles, I have already traveled 319 miles. How much farther do I have to travel?

Some students visualize a problem like this as adding up from the distance traveled to the total distance, while others visualize subtracting the distance traveled from the total distance. This provides another opportunity for students to consider the relationship between addition and subtraction.

$319 +$ ______ $= 631$

$631 - 319 =$ ______

The Algebra Connections page in the curriculum unit that focuses on addition and subtraction (Unit 5) shows how students are applying the inverse relationship between addition and subtraction as they solve problems. It also highlights the algebraic ideas that underlie the generalizations students investigate and articulate when they create equivalent expressions in order to solve a problem (e.g., $124 - 89 = 125 - 90$).

Mathematical Emphases

The Base-Ten Number System

- Extending knowledge of the base-ten number system to 10,000

Computational Fluency

- Adding and subtracting accurately and efficiently

Whole Number Operations

- Describing, analyzing, and comparing strategies for adding and subtracting whole numbers
- Understanding different types of subtraction problems

Benchmarks

- Read, write, and sequence numbers up to 10,000.
- Add and subtract multiples of 10 (including multiples of 100 and 1,000) fluently.
- Solve addition problems efficiently, choosing from a variety of strategies.
- Solve subtraction problems with 3-digit numbers by using at least one strategy efficiently.

Number and Operations: Rational Numbers

The major focus of the work on rational numbers is on building students' understanding of the meaning, order, and equivalencies of fractions and decimals. Students continue to focus on the meaning of fractions as equal parts of a whole. They extend their images of equal parts to accommodate fractions that are greater than 1. Students work with fractions in the context of area (equal parts of a rectangle), as a group of things (e.g., a fractional part of the class), and on a number line. They work with fractions that represent halves, thirds, fourths, fifths, sixths, eighths, tenths, and twelfths.

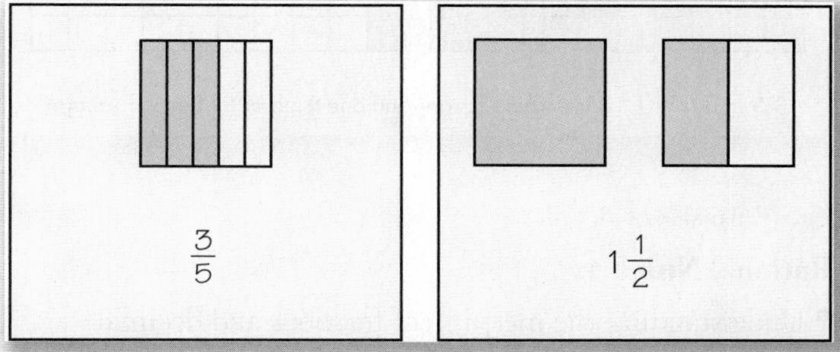

Students are introduced to decimal fractions in tenths and hundredths as an extension of the place value system they have studied for whole numbers. They relate decimals to equivalent decimals and fractions (for example, when they represent 0.25 as part of a rectangle, they can see how it is equal to $\frac{1}{4}$ and to $2\frac{1}{2}$ tenths). Students draw on their mental images of fractions and decimals and on their knowledge of fraction and decimal equivalencies and relationships to reason about fraction comparisons, to order fractions on a number line, and to add fractions and decimals using representations.

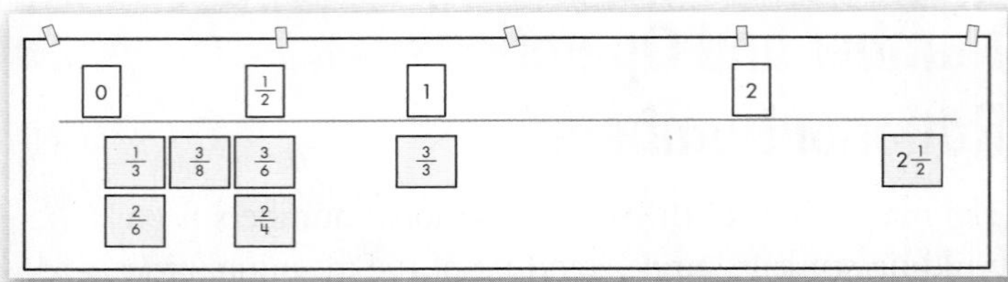

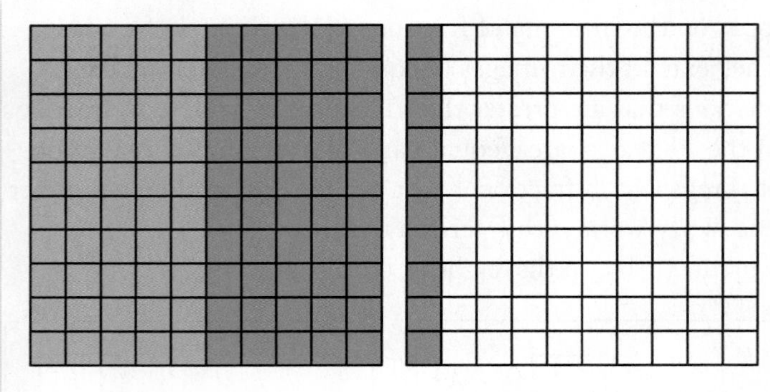

0.5 + 0.6 = 1.1 (one whole square and one tenth of the second square)

Mathematical Emphases

Rational Numbers

- Understanding the meaning of fractions and decimal fractions
- Comparing the values of fractions and decimal fractions

Computation with Rational Numbers

- Using representations to add rational numbers

Benchmarks

- Identify fractional parts of an area.
- Identify fractional parts of a group (of objects, people, etc.).
- Read, write, and interpret fraction notation.
- Order fractions with like and unlike denominators.
- Read, write, and interpret decimal fractions in tenths and hundredths.

Patterns, Functions, and Change

In Grade 4, students use graphs and tables to represent change. One focus of their work is how a line graph shows the *rate of change,* as they consider questions such as the following:

How does this graph show the parts of the story that are about *speed* and the parts of the story that are about *changes in speed*?

What was the rate of growth for this plant? When was it growing more slowly or more quickly?

Day	Height
Thursday	3 cm
Friday	4 cm
Monday	10 cm
Tuesday	13.5 cm
Wednesday	15 cm
Thursday	16 cm
Friday	16.5 cm
Monday	17 cm

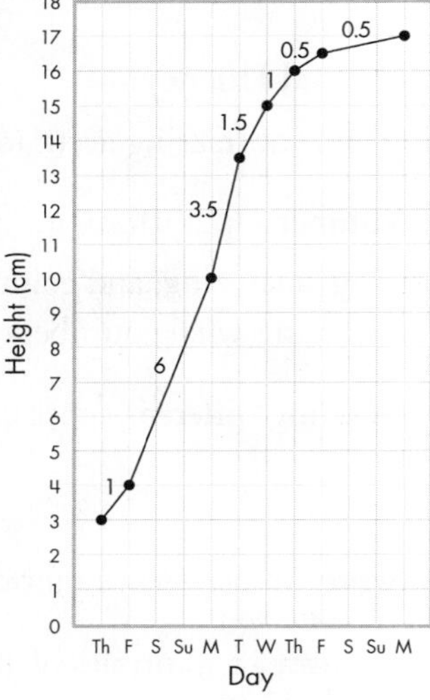

Students create tables and graphs for situations with a constant rate of change and use them to compare related situations.

Penny Jar A has 8 pennies in the jar to start and 2 pennies are added in each round. Penny Jar B has 0 pennies in the jar to start and 4 pennies are added in each round. Will the number of pennies in Penny Jar B, which starts with fewer pennies, ever "catch up" to the number of pennies in Penny Jar A?

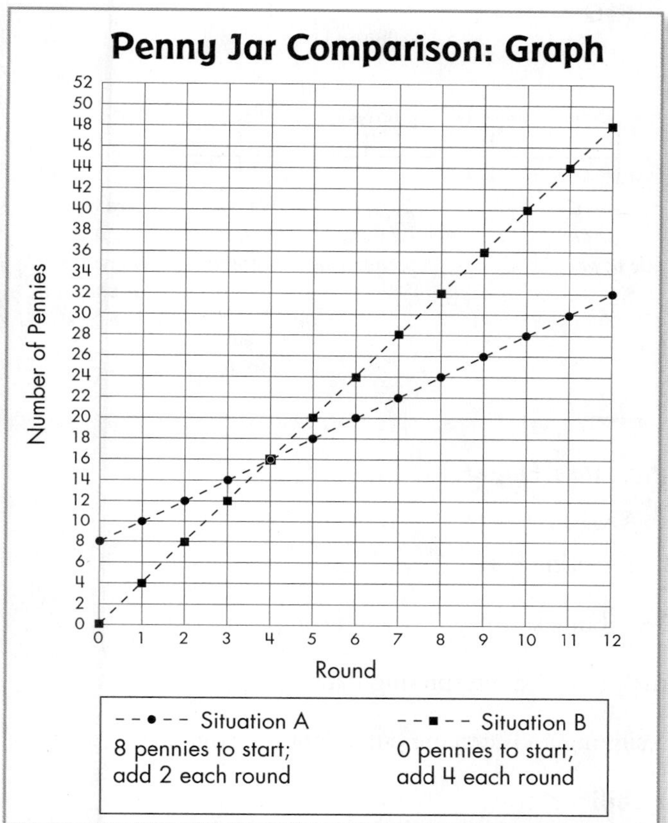

By analyzing tables and graphs, students consider how the starting amount and the rate of change define the relationship between the two quantities (e.g., number of rounds, total number of pennies) and develop rules that govern that relationship. Students initially articulate these rules in words (as they did in Grade 3), but they also are introduced to the use of symbolic notation and equations to represent their rules. They use these rules to determine the value of one variable when the value of the other is known.

How many pennies are in Penny Jar A after 10 rounds?

Mathematical Emphases

Using Tables and Graphs

- Using graphs to represent change
- Using tables to represent change

Linear Change

- Describing and representing a constant rate of change

Benchmarks

- Connect tables and graphs to each other and to the situations they represent.
- Make a graph on a coordinate grid from a table of values.
- Describe how a graph shows change: where the rate of change is increasing, decreasing, or remaining constant and how differences in steepness represent differences in the rate of change.
- Take into account the starting amount and the amount of change in describing and comparing situations of constant change.
- In a situation of constant change, write rules (using words or arithmetic expressions) to determine the value of one quantity, given the value of the other.

Data Analysis and Probability

Students continue to develop their understanding of data analysis by collecting, representing, describing, and interpreting numerical data to answer a question, investigate an issue, or provide information about something in the world that is of interest. Their work focuses on describing and summarizing data for comparing two groups. Using a *line plot* as a tool for showing the shape or distribution of a set of data—where the data are concentrated, how they are spread across the range—students represent data about two groups and then consider how to characterize how the groups are similar or different. They develop conclusions and make arguments, based on the evidence they have collected.

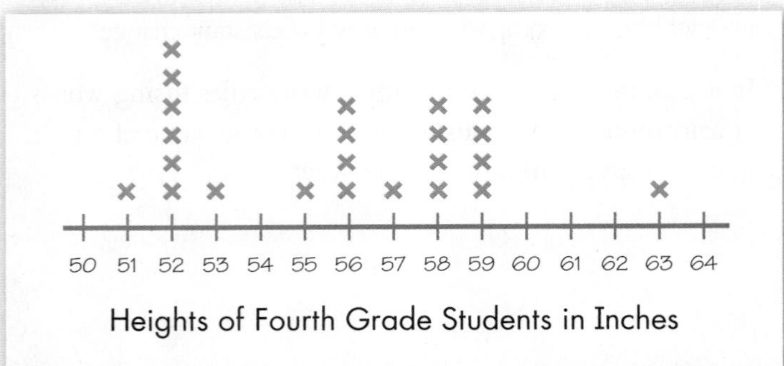

Line plot of student height

Students also work on describing and predicting the likelihood of events in their world: What events are impossible, unlikely, likely, or certain? They consider situations in which there is a known number of possible outcomes—such as when rolling a number cube or pulling a red cube out of a bag holding a certain number of red and blue cubes. Students reason about how the theoretical chance (or *theoretical probability*) of, for example, rolling 1 on a number cube compares to what actually happens when a number cube is rolled repeatedly.

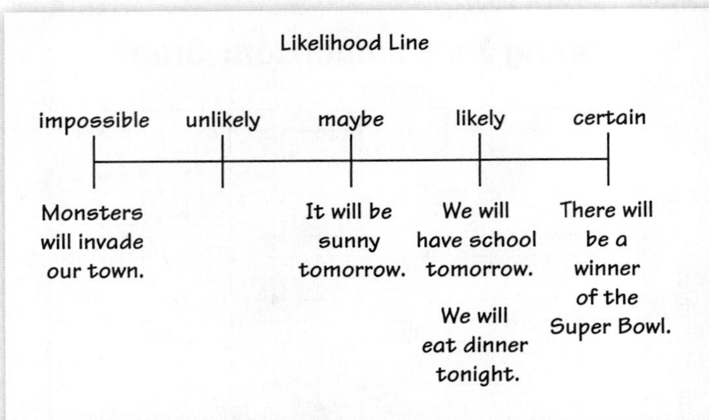

Mathematical Emphases

Data Analysis

- Representing data
- Describing, summarizing, and comparing data
- Analyzing and interpreting data
- Designing and carrying out a data investigation

Probability

- Describing the probability of an event

Benchmarks

- Design an effective survey question to compare two groups.
- Organize and represent data about two groups in order to compare the groups.
- Describe the shape of the data from a numerical data set, including where the data are concentrated and the highest, lowest, and median values.
- Use data to compare two groups.
- Use evidence from a set of data to support an argument.
- Describe the likelihood of an event in terms of a scale from impossible (probability of 0) to certain (probability of 1).

Geometry and Measurement

Students expand their understanding of the attributes of two-dimensional (2-D) and three-dimensional (3-D) shapes and how these attributes determine their classification. Students consider the various attributes of 2-D shapes, such as the number of sides, the length of sides, parallel sides, and the size of angles, expanding their knowledge of four-sided figures (quadrilaterals) to include parallelograms, rhombuses, and trapezoids.

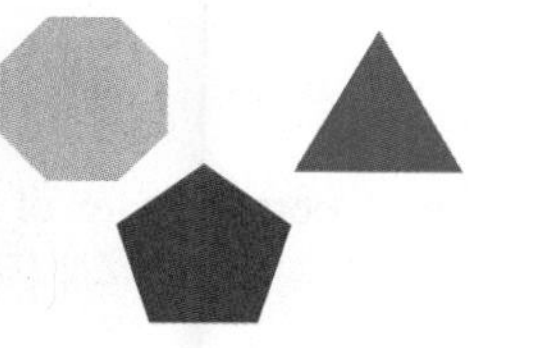

Polygons

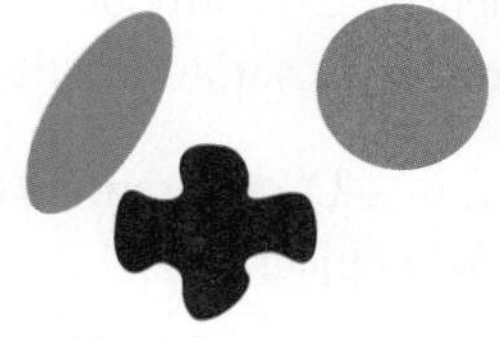

Not Polygons

Students also describe attributes and properties of geometric solids (3-D shapes), such as the shape and number of faces, the number and relative lengths of edges, and the number of vertices. They describe classes of shapes, for example, how a pyramid has triangular faces meeting at a point.

They visualize how 3-D shapes can be represented in two dimensions, for example, by silhouettes projected by 3-D objects and structures.

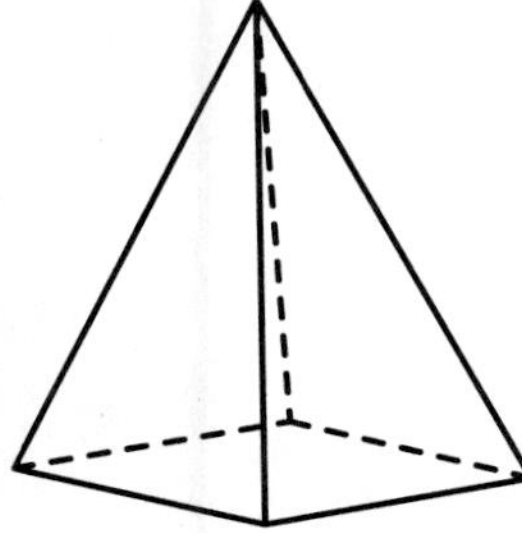

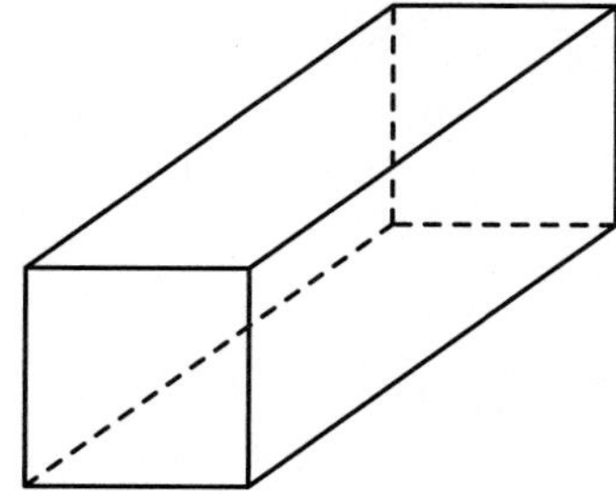

In Grade 4, students continue to build on measurement work from earlier grades, which includes linear measurement, area, angle measurement, and volume. They use both U.S. standard units (inches, feet, and yards) and metric units (centimeters and meters) to measure lengths up to 100 feet, and they determine the perimeter of various shapes.

They measure the area of both regular and nonregular polygons in square units by using the understanding that area can be decomposed—that is, broken into smaller parts.

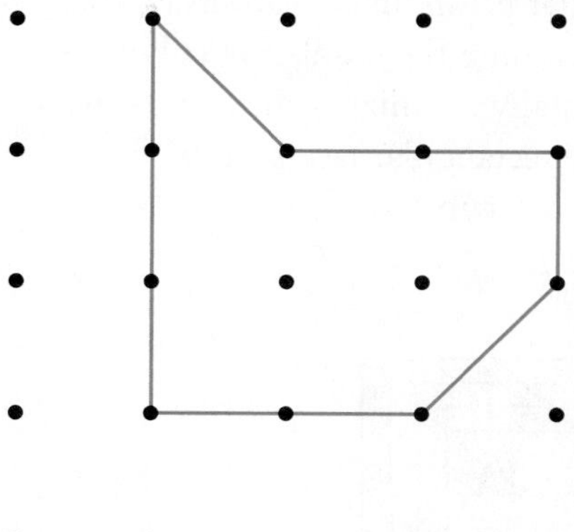

Measuring area on the Geoboard

Students work on determining the size of angles relative to a right angle, or 90 degrees. For instance, if three equal angles form a right angle, then each of the smaller angles must be $\frac{1}{3}$ of 90 degrees or 30 degrees.

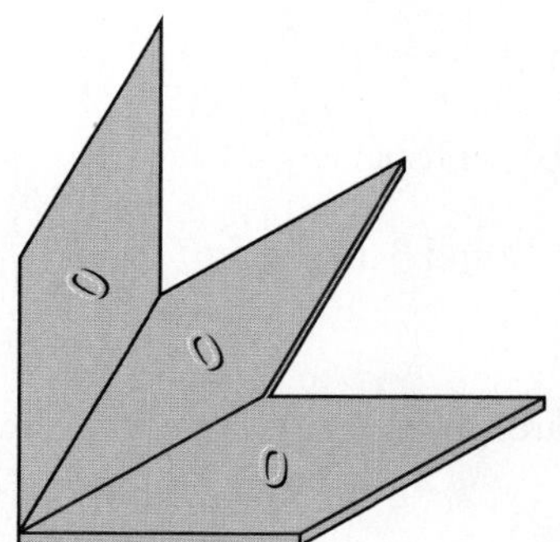

A right angle formed with Power Polygons

Finally, students work on understanding volume by structuring and determining the volume of one kind of geometric solid, a rectangular prism, in cubic units. They develop strategies for determining the number of cubes in 3-D arrays of cubes by mentally organizing the cubes—for example, as a stack of three rectangular layers, each composed of three rows of four cubes.

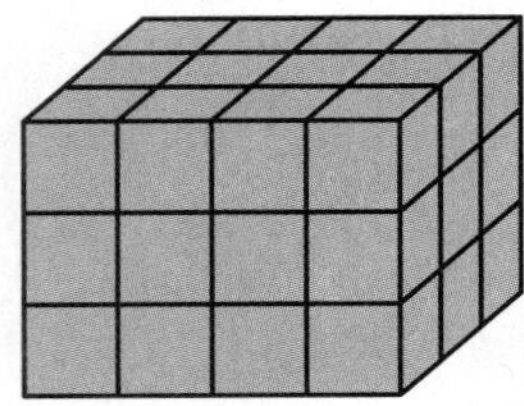

Mathematical Emphases

Features of Shape

- Describing and classifying 2-D figures
- Describing and measuring angles
- Describing properties of 3-D shapes
- Translating between 2-D and 3-D shapes

Linear Measurement

- Measuring with standard units

Area Measurement

- Finding and understanding area

Volume

- Structuring rectangular prisms and determining their volume

Benchmarks

- Use appropriate measurement tools to measure distance.
- Identify quadrilaterals as any four-sided closed shape.
- Know that a right angle measures 90 degrees and use this as a landmark to find angles of 30, 45, and 60 degrees.
- Find the area of polygons using a square unit of measure.
- Identify 2-D silhouettes of 3-D solids (e.g., a cone can project a triangular silhouette).
- Draw 2-D representations showing different perspectives of a 3-D object.
- Find the volume of cube buildings and rectangular prisms.

PART 4

Ten-Minute Math

Curriculum Unit	1	2	3	4	5	6	7	8	9
Ten-Minute Math									
Counting Around the Class	●		●					●	
Closest Estimate								●	●
Practicing Place Value					●	●	●		
Quick Images	●		●	●			●		
Quick Survey		●				●			●
Today's Number	●	●		●	●				

Preview

Ten-Minute Math activities appear throughout Grades 3–5. These short activities, designed to take no longer than 10–15 minutes, support and balance the in-depth work of each curriculum unit. After their first introduction in a math session, they are intended for use outside of math time. Some teachers use them to bring the whole class together just before or after lunch or recess or at the beginning or end of the day.

At Grade 4, six Ten-Minute Math activities are woven through the nine curriculum units. The following pages contain complete procedures for these activities, including the variations intended for use in Grade 4. Specific suggestions for use are found in Today's Plan for each session. It is recommended that you begin with the suggested daily problems and adapt them to fit the needs of your students throughout the year. Any needed preparation is noted in the Investigation Planner.

Counting Around the Class

Students count around the class by a particular number such as 2, 5, or 9. If students count by 2, the first student says "2," the next student says "4," the next "6," and so on. Before the count starts, students try to estimate the ending number of the count, the number the last person in the class will say. During and after the count, students discuss the relationships between the chosen factor and its multiples.

Math Focus Points

Students practice counting by different numbers and reason about the relationships among factors and their multiples.

- Finding the multiples of numbers through skip counting
- Becoming familiar with multiplication patterns
- Understanding the relationship between skip counting and multiplication
- Using the nearest landmark to find multiples of a given number
- Relating factors to their multiples

Counting Around the Class is introduced in Session 3.1 in Unit 1, *Factors, Multiples, and Arrays;* it also appears in Unit 3, *Multiple Towers and Division Stories;* and in Unit 8, *How Many Packages? How Many Groups?*

Basic Activity

Step 1 Choose a number to count by. For example, if the class has been working with quarters recently, you might want to count by 25.

Step 2 Ask students to estimate the target number.

If we count around the class by 25, what number will the last person in the class say?

Encourage students to talk about how they could determine the last number without actually counting.

Step 3 Count around the class by your chosen number. "25, . . . 50, . . . 75, ..." If some students seem uncertain about what number comes next, consider writing the numbers on the board as students say them. Seeing visual patterns often helps students with the spoken pattern.

You might also count around a second time by the same number, starting with a different person, so that students hear the same pattern more than once and have their turns at different points in the sequence.

Step 4 Pause in the middle of the count to look back. To help students think about the relationship between a factor and its multiples, ask questions such as the following:

We're up to 375, counting by 25. How many students have counted so far? How do you know?

Step 5 Extend the problem. Ask questions like the following:

Which of your estimations were reasonable? Which were possible? Which were impossible? (A student might remark, for example, "You can't have 510 for 25s because 25 lands only on the 25s, the 50s, the 75s, and the 100s.")

What if we had 32 students in this class instead of 28? What would the ending number be?

What if we counted by a different number? This time we counted by 25 and ended on 700. What if we counted by 50? What do you think the ending number would be? Why do you think it would be twice as big? How did you figure that out?

Whenever you introduce an unfamiliar number to count by, some students may need some preparation before they begin counting around the class. Ask students to work in pairs, with whatever materials they want, to determine the ending for the count.

Be sensitive to the possibility that some students may be embarrassed or feel "put on the spot" because of the structure of the activity. Some teachers allow students to volunteer for the next number, rather than counting in a particular order. Other teachers make the count a cooperative effort, establishing an atmosphere in which students readily help each other, and where anyone feels free to ask for help.

Variations

What Could We Count By?

Specify a target number such as 24, 50, 72, 100, or 1,000. Ask:

What number (or numbers) could we count by so someone in our class would land on (25)?

Encourage students to share their strategies for figuring this out. Count around the class by the suggested numbers to see if they work.

Counting Backward

Starting with a given number, count backward around the class. Choose numbers with patterns that are already familiar to students. For example, start at 400 and count backward by 2, 5, 10, or 25. As students become more comfortable with this variation, try counting by more difficult numbers.

Alternatively, play a modified version of *What Could We Count By?* Give students a starting number (such as 100 or 1,000) and ask them to find a number they could count by, backward, that would land exactly on 0 (or so that someone would say a particular number during the count).

Closest Estimate

Given a computation problem and three estimates, students pick the closest estimate by computing mentally.

Math Focus Points

Closest Estimate provides practice in estimating answers to computation problems by changing numbers to a landmark and multiplying by 10 for easier computation.

- Approximating numbers to nearby landmark numbers, for example, multiples of 10 or 100
- Calculating mentally
- Comparing answer choices to find the one closest to the actual answer

Materials

- Overhead projector or chart paper
- Transparencies T82–83, T90–93, *Closest Estimate*

How Many Packages? How Many Groups?

Closest Estimate (page 1 of 2)

1. 19 × 21 ≈	40	400	2,000
2. 38 × 12 ≈	380	450	1,000
3. 21 × 33 ≈	60	600	1,000
4. 42 × 18 ≈	420	800	840
5. 54 × 23 ≈	100	500	1,000
6. 60 × 27 ≈	1,200	1,600	2,000
7. 23 × 84 ≈	160	1,600	16,000
8. 57 × 32 ≈	1,500	1,800	2,100

T82

▲ Closest Estimate transparency

Closest Estimate is introduced in Session 1.1 in Unit 8, *How Many Packages? How Many Groups?* it also appears in Unit 9, *Penny Jars and Plant Growth.*

Basic Activity

Step 1 Present the problem. Show students the problem and the possible estimates, one at a time, and give them about 30 seconds to consider which estimate is closest to the actual answer.

Step 2 Discuss strategies. Collect a few responses and discuss any disagreements. Students should defend their answer choices by explaining how they made their estimate. Ask questions like the following:

How did you change the numbers to make the problem easier?

Why do you think that this estimate is closer than this one?

Is this estimate more or less than the actual answer? How do you know?

Variations

Students Invent Their Own Problems

Students prepare problems with a choice of estimates. Guide students to use numbers that are near landmark numbers in their problems. Encourage them to include possible estimates that seem reasonable but not close to the intended answer. They then exchange their problems with others and compare their strategies.

Suggest that students use the same numbers and write addition and multiplication problems. Students may notice that there is a greater range in possible "good answers" for two problems using the same numbers but different operations. For example:

726 + 1,177 =	**1,800**	**1,900**	**2,000**	**8,300**
726 × 1,177 =	**8,400**	**80,000**	**700,000**	**800,000**

Practicing Place Value

Students practice reading and writing numbers up to 10,000. Then students add 10 and multiples of 10 to or subtract 10 and multiples of 10 from the given numbers. Students discuss how the values of the digits change in each equation.

Math Focus Points

Students focus on how numbers are composed and how written numerals relate to the quantity they represent.

- Recognizing and interpreting the value of each digit in 3- and 4-digit numbers
- Reading and writing numbers up to 10,000
- Adding multiples of 10 to and subtracting multiples of 10 from 3- and 4-digit numbers
- Reading and writing decimal fractions and decimal numbers
- Adding tenths and hundredths to, and subtracting them from decimal fractions and decimal numbers.

Practicing Place Value is introduced in Session 1.3 in Unit 5, *Landmarks and Large Numbers;* it also appears in Unit 6, *Fraction Cards and Decimal Squares;* and in Unit 7, *Moving Between Solids and Silhouettes.*

Materials

- Blank paper and pencil
- 10 × 10 squares (as needed for *Decimal Fractions* variation)

Basic Activity

Step 1 Write or say a number. Your choice of number will depend on the size of the numbers your students are working on or need work with. Alternate between writing the numbers on the board and reading them aloud. For example, write 835 or say "eight hundred thirty-five."

Step 2 Students say or write the number. Give all students an opportunity to read, write, and say this number correctly. Ask a volunteer to say or write the number for the whole class.

Step 3 Add or subtract multiples of 10. Write or say a series of addition and/or subtraction problems, adding or subtracting multiples of 10 (ten or hundreds) to the starting number. For example,

What is 835 + 20? 835 + 40? 835 + 60? 835 + 100? 835 + 200? 835 + 300?

or

What is 835 + 40? 835 − 20? 835 + 30? 835 − 30? 835 − 100? 835 − 200?

Step 4 Students mentally solve the problems. As students share their solutions, record the equations (e.g., 835 + 20 = 855, 835 − 200 = 635), or have a student record them, on the board.

Step 5 Discuss place value. Ask students to compare each sum or difference with the starting number (for example, for the problem 835 + 20, compare 855 and 835). Ask:

What was the effect of adding the multiple to [or subtracting the multiple from] the starting number?

Which places in the two numbers have the same digits?

Which places do not? Why?

Step 6 If time remains, pose additional similar problems.

Variations

Decimal Numbers

In this variation, the basic procedure stays the same, but students practice adding multiples of 10 to and subtracting multiples of 10 from decimal numbers (e.g., 356.4 + 20, 356.4 − 20, 356.4 + 200, 356.4 − 200). Alternatively, students practice adding multiples of tenths to and subtracting them from decimal numbers (e.g., 56.4 + 0.1, 56.4 + 0.3, 56.4 + 0.4). As with the basic procedure, have students compare each sum or difference with the starting number and identify how the places have changed and why.

Decimal Fractions

Write a decimal fraction (a number less than 1) on the board, for example, 0.4. Students then practice saying the number, using both common ways of reading decimals, in this case, "four tenths" or "zero point four." Ask questions like the following:

What is *2 tenths more* than this number?

What is *2 hundredths more* than this number?

What is *1 hundredth less*?

Make 10 × 10 squares available to students as they participate in this activity.

How Many 10s? How Many 100s? How Many 1,000s?

In this variation, students decompose numbers by place. However, it is more than just naming the number in each place. It includes understanding, for example, that while 335 is 3 hundreds, 3 tens, and 5 ones, it is also 2 hundreds, 13 tens, and 5 ones; or 1 hundred, 23 tens, and 5 ones; or 33 tens and 5 ones.

Step 1 Write or say a number. Write a number on the board (or say it and have students write it). For example:

1,835

Step 2 Ask: **"How many groups of ____ (10, 100, 1,000, etc.) are in the number?** For example, ask students how many groups of hundreds are in 1,835. If students think that eight is the only answer, ask them to consider a context such as money.

If this were money, how many hundred dollar bills would we have if we had $1,835?

Establish with students that there are 18 hundreds in 1,835.

Step 3 Pose additional problems with the same number. Ask students to fill in the blanks in the following sums for 1,835 and explain how they figured out the value:

____ thousands + 8 hundreds + 3 tens + 5 ones

1 thousands + ____ hundreds + 3 tens + 5 ones

1 thousands + 6 hundreds + ____ tens + 5 ones

Then ask students to make up five different combinations of place values that equal 1,835: 15 hundreds + 33 tens + 5 ones; 16 hundreds + 23 tens + 5 ones; and so on.

Quick Images

In this activity, students visualize and analyze images of geometric figures. After briefly viewing an image of a two-dimensional (2-D) design or three-dimensional (3-D) structure, students either draw it or build it from the mental image they formed during the brief viewing. They might see it as a whole ("it looks like a box, three cubes long and two cubes high") or decompose it into memorable parts ("it looks like four triangles—right side up, then upside down, then right side up, then upside down").

Math Focus Points

Students visualize and reconstruct geometric images (of 2-D geometric designs or 3-D cube structures), either as a whole or by decomposing them into memorable parts.

- Organizing and analyzing visual images
- Developing language and concepts needed to communicate about spatial relationships

Quick Images is introduced in Session 2.1 in Unit 1, *Factors, Multiples, and Arrays;* it also appears in Unit 3, *Multiple Towers and Division Stories;* in Unit 4, *Size, Shape, and Symmetry;* and in Unit 7, *Moving Between Solids and Silhouettes.*

Materials

- Overhead projector
- Transparencies T24–T25, T34–T39, T42–T44, T74–T76, *Quick Images*

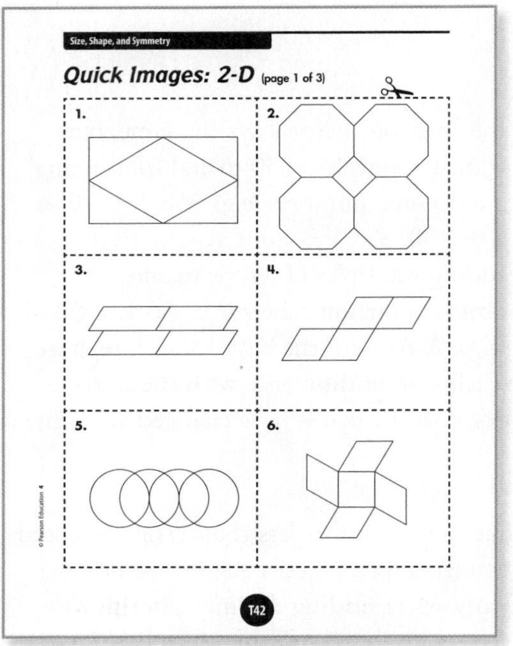

▲ Resource Masters, Unit 4 M10 Transparencies, T42

Basic Activity

Step 1 Flash an image for 3 seconds. It is important to show the figure for as close to 3 seconds as possible. If you show it too long, students will draw or build from the figure rather than from their mental image of it; if you show it too briefly, they will not have sufficient time to form a mental image. Students quickly learn to study the figure carefully while it is visible so they can draw or build it from their mental image.

Step 2 Students draw or build what they saw. Give students a few minutes with the relevant materials (paper and pencil, cubes) to draw or construct a figure that matches the mental image they formed. When you see that most students have finished working, proceed to step 3.

Step 3 Flash the image again for 3 seconds, this time for revision. After showing the same image for another 3 seconds, students revise their drawings or structures according to what they see in this second viewing. It is essential to provide enough time here, before a third showing, for most students to complete their attempts at drawing or building. While they may not have completed their figures, they should have done all they can until they see the image displayed again. When student work subsides, proceed to step 4.

Step 4 Show the image a third and final time. This time leave the image visible so that all students can complete or revise their drawings or structures.

Step 5 Discuss the mental images students formed. Students explain the different ways they saw the figure as they looked at it on successive "flashes." Encourage students to explain what relationships they used in decomposing the figure.

Variations

Quick Images: Seeing Numbers

Quick Images: Seeing Numbers is introduced in Session 2.1 in Unit 1, *Factors, Multiples, and Arrays.*

Materials

- Transparencies T24–T25, T34–T39, *Quick Images: Seeing Numbers*
- Blank paper and pencil

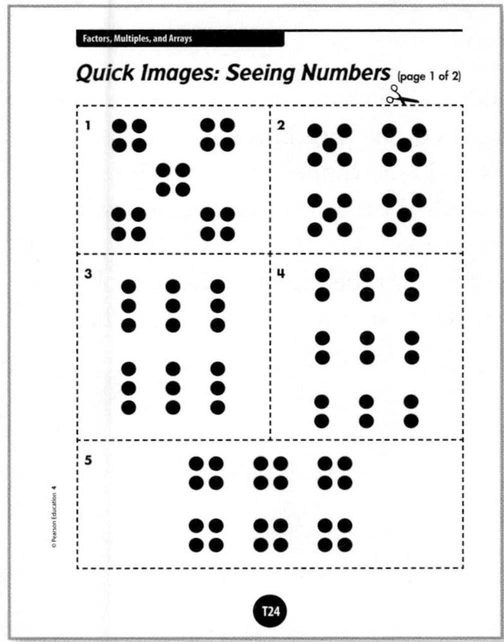

▲ Resource Masters, Unit 1 M33; Transparencies, T24

Math Focus Points

- Writing equations to describe dot patterns

Following the procedure for the basic activity, students determine the number of dots in an image and write an equation to represent how they organized their counting. Some students may want to draw a mental image of the arrangement to get a clearer picture of it. To help students describe their mental images and write an equation, ask questions such as the following:

How were the dots arranged?

How many dots were in each group?

How many groups were there?

Quick Images: 2-D

Quick Images: 2-D is introduced in Session 2.1 in Unit 4, *Size, Shape, and Symmetry.*

Materials

- Transparencies T42–T44, *Quick Images: 2-D*
- Blank paper and pencil

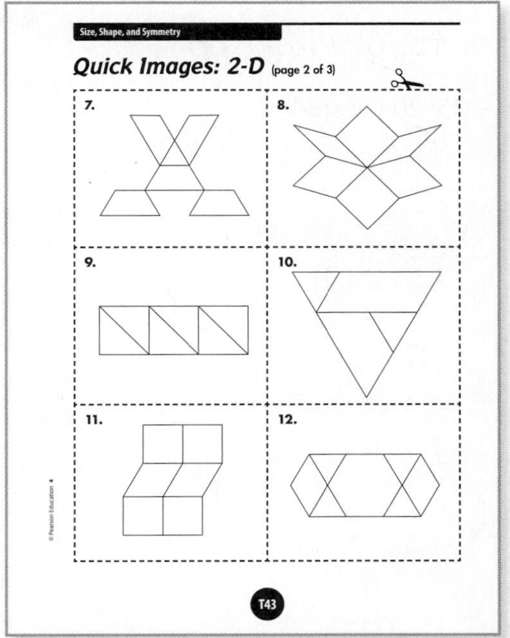

▲ Resource Masters, Unit 4 M11; Transparencies, T43

Math Focus Points

- Decomposing images of 2-D shapes and then recombining them to make a given design

Following the procedure for the basic activity, students use paper and pencil to draw the 2-D designs they see.

When talking about what they saw in successive flashes, many students will say things like "I saw four triangles in a row." For students having difficulty, suggest the following:

Each design is made from familiar geometric shapes. Find these shapes and try to determine how they are put together.

As students describe their figures, you can introduce the correct geometric terms for component shapes. As you use these terms naturally in class discussion, students will begin to recognize and use them more frequently and accurately.

Quick Images: 3-D

Quick Images: 3-D is introduced in Session 1.3 in Unit 7, *Moving Between Solids and Silhouettes.*

Materials

- Transparencies T74–T76, *Quick Images: 3-D*
- Connecting cubes (15–20 per student)

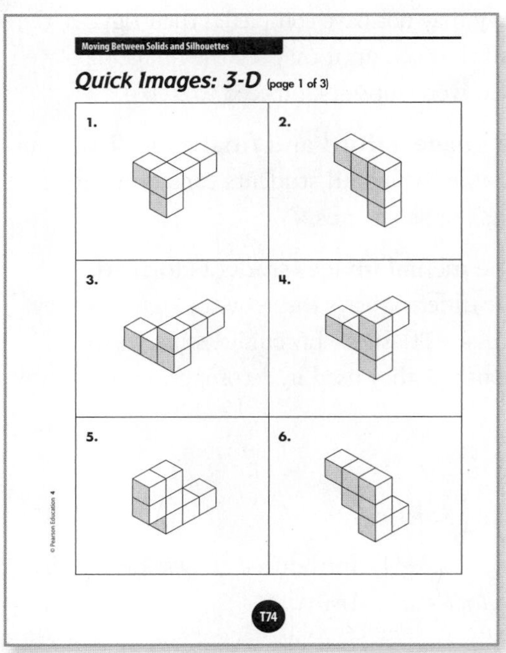

▲ Resource Masters, Unit 7 M11; Transparencies, T74

Math Focus Points

- Decomposing images of 3-D shapes and then recombining them to make a given structure

For this version, students follow the procedure in the basic activity to build images of the cube buildings they see. Each student will need 15–20 connecting cubes. Several of the cube figures on the transparency are intentionally ambiguous, as some unseen cubes "in the back" may or may not be a part of the figure. Students with differing solutions should have an opportunity to compare and defend their constructions.

Quick Survey

Quick Survey gives students many opportunities to quickly collect, graph, describe, and interpret data about themselves and the world around them. Students collect data to investigate a question about themselves. The data can be organized as a line plot, a list, a table, or a bar graph. Then students describe what they can tell from the data, generate some new questions, and, if appropriate, make predictions about what will happen the next time they collect the same data.

Math Focus Points

Students collect, organize, describe, and interpret data.

- Describing features of the data
- Interpreting and posing questions about the data

Quick Survey first appears in Session 1.4 in Unit 2, *Describing the Shape of the Data;* it also appears in Unit 6, *Fraction Cards and Decimal Squares;* and in Unit 9, *Penny Jars and Plant Growth.*

Materials

- Chart paper or overhead projector
- Marking pen

Basic Activity

Step 1 Choose a question. Use the question suggested or use your own question, which can also be provided by the students. Make sure the question involves data that students know or can observe. Here are some examples:

How many buttons are you wearing today?
What is the best thing you ate yesterday?
Are you wearing shoes or sneakers or sandals?
How did you get to school today?
What is your favorite fruit?
What do you usually eat for breakfast?

Step 2 Quickly collect and display the data. Use a list, a table, a line plot, or a bar graph. For example, a bar graph for data about how students get to school could look something like this:

How Do You Get to School?

Bus	Walk	Car	Bike
	Gerry		
	Victor		
Tamara	Cole		
Beth	Yusef		
LaShon	David		
Karen	Henry	Evan	
Molly	Connie	Jonas	April
Ube	Ophelia	Aida	Jessica
Joey	Vipin	Thomas	Ethan
Nishit	Maria	Marcus	Antwon

Step 3 Ask students to describe the data. What do they notice? For data that have a numerical order (e.g., How many buttons do you have today? How many people live in your house? How many months until your birthday?), ask questions like the following:

Are the data spread out or close together?

What are the highest and lowest values?

Where do most of the data seem to fall?

What seems typical or usual for this class?

For data in categories (e.g., What is your favorite book? How do you get to school? What month is your birthday?), ask questions like the following:

Which categories have a lot of data? . . . few data? . . . none?

Is there a way to categorize the data differently to get other information?

Step 4 Ask students to interpret and predict.

Why do you think that the data came out this way?

Does anything about the data surprise you?

Do you think we would get similar data if we collected it tomorrow? next week? in another class? with adults?

Step 5 List any new questions. Keep a running list of questions you can use for further data collection and analysis. You may want to ask some of these questions again.

Note that students take surveys about "favorites"—for example, flavor of ice cream, breakfast cereal, book, color—or other data that fall into categories, the graphs are often flat and uninteresting. There is not too much to say, for example, about a graph like this:

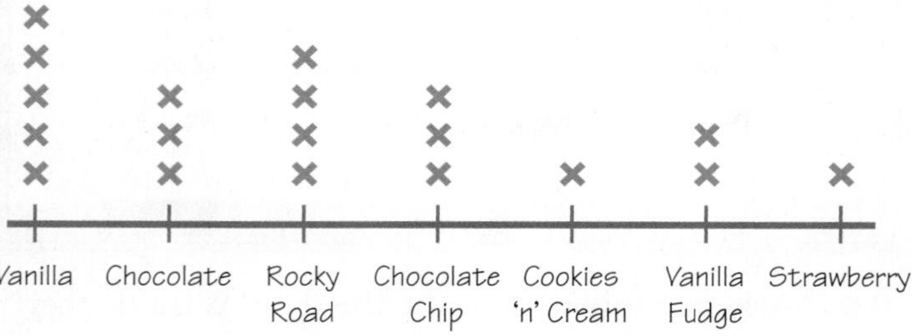

It is more interesting for students to group their results into more descriptive categories so that they can see other things about the data. In this case, even though vanilla seems to be the favorite in this graph, another way for grouping the data seems to show that flavors with some chocolate in them are really the favorites:

Flavors with chocolate: 𝍸 𝍸 |||

Flavors without chocolate: 𝍸 |

Variations

Data from Home

Students might collect data by asking questions or making observations at home:

What time do your brothers and sisters go to bed?
How many states (or how many countries) have you visited?
How many cousins do you have?

Students bring in their answers to use in the class activity.

Data from Another Class or Other Teachers

Depending on your school situation, you may be able to assign students to collect data from other classrooms or other teachers. Students are always interested in surveying others about questions that interest them, such as this one for teachers: When you were in fifth grade, what did you like best about school?

Today's Number

Students write several different expressions that equal a given number. They do so in the context of constraints that define the operations and number relationships they can use. Constraints on what numbers or operations students can use encourage students to be flexible in their use of arithmetic skills and provide a focus on the particular number or computation work that students need to develop or practice.

Math Focus Points

Today's Number provides computation practice and an opportunity for students to demonstrate flexibility in a variety of expressions that equal a given number.

- Generating equivalent expressions for a number using particular constraints
- Practicing computation skills
- Using notation to record expressions

Today's Number first appears in Investigation 1 in Unit 1, *Factors, Multiples, and Arrays,* but it is not formally introduced in a session. It also appears in Unit 2, *Describing the Shape of the Data*; Unit 4, *Size, Shape, and Symmetry*; and in Unit 5, *Landmarks and Large Numbers.*

Materials

- Blank paper and pencil
- Chart paper and markers

Basic Activity

Step 1 Record today's number. Write the number chosen for the day at the top of the chart paper.

Step 2 Define and record the constraint(s). Define the constraints and record them on the chart paper.

For example, here are some constraints that offer students addition and subtraction practice in Grade 4:

- Use one or more multiples of 10.
- Use only subtraction.
- Use both addition and subtraction in each expression.
- Use at least three numbers.
- Use one or more combinations that add to 100.

Step 3 Students write expressions. Give students a few minutes to write expressions that equal today's number.

Step 4 List the expressions that students suggest. Use the chart paper to record students' expressions. As you do so, invite the rest of the class to confirm each suggestion or to discuss any incorrect responses and explain their thinking.

Teaching Note

Use of Parentheses

Students often write expressions that contain more than one operation. Explain to students that there are rules about solving equations with more than one operation. Using the order of operations, $4 + 3 \times 5 = 19$ because multiplication is solved before addition. Parentheses are used to indicate which part of the problem should be solved first. Show students how using parentheses in different parts of the equation can result in a different answer: for example, $4 + (3 \times 5) = 19$ or $(4 + 3) \times 5 = 35$.

Variations

Looking for Patterns

Encourage students to find expressions that they can alter systematically to find more expressions. For example, here is a pattern that a student devised for 100.

2×50

$2 \times 49 + 2$

$2 \times 48 + 4$

$2 \times 47 + 6$

$2 \times 46 + 8$

Broken Calculator

Broken Calculator is introduced in Session 1.1 in Unit 2, *Describing the Shape of the Data;* it also appears in Unit 4, *Size, Shape, and Symmetry;* and in Unit 5, *Landmarks and Large Numbers.* In this variation, students work to make a number appear on their calculator display without using particular keys, which are said to be "broken." The broken keys can be operations, numbers, or both.

Materials

- Calculators *(optional)*

Note that *Broken Calculator* can be done with or without the use of calculators. If students have calculators, ask them to write the appropriate expression first and then use the calculator to check that their solution results in the given number. If students do not have calculators, they can be told to imagine that they are using a calculator to create the number.

For example, when posing a problem, say,

I want to make 35 using my calculator, but the 3 key and the 5 key are broken. How can I use my calculator to do this task?

Possible constraints for *Broken Calculator* include the following:

Restricting Number Keys

- Students make numbers without using the digits in those numbers, for example:

  Make 1,000 without using a 1 or a 0.

  998 + 2
  997 + 3
  996 + 4

Restricting Operation Keys

- Students make a number without using multiplication or division.

- Students make a number using only multiplication and division.

- Students make a number using only subtraction.

Restricting Both Operations and Keys

- Make the missing operations problems more challenging by not allowing students to use any of the digits in the final number. For example,

  Make 654 using only addition and subtraction and without using the digits 6, 5, or 4.

PART 5

Technology in *Investigations*

Preview

The *Investigations* curriculum incorporates two forms of technology: calculators and computers. Calculators are assumed to be standard mathematical tools, available for student use as appropriate. Computers, on the other hand, are explicitly linked to one curriculum unit at each grade level through software that is provided with the curriculum.

Using Calculators with the Curriculum

Students should become comfortable using a basic calculator as a tool that is common in their homes and communities. Increasingly sophisticated calculators are being developed and used in settings ranging from high school mathematics courses to science, business, and construction. Students need to learn how to use the calculator effectively and appropriately as a tool, just as they need to learn to read a clock, interpret a map, measure with a ruler, or use coins. They should use calculators for sensible purposes—just as you would do—not as a replacement for mental calculations or for pencil and paper calculations they are learning to do. Encourage students to use calculators to double-check calculations, as an aid if they have many calculations to carry out outside of math class, or to solve problems for which they can think out a solution but don't yet have the experience to carry out the computation.

Calculators are recommended for a few specific activities in curriculum units. For most of the work on number and operations, students are using their own representations and reasoning to solve problems as they develop computational fluency. Calculators might sometimes be used for double-checking, although students should also be able to double-check their work without a calculator.

Look for situations in the classroom when the purpose of the mathematical activity is not the development of computational fluency and when the numbers and calculations are beyond the students' skills in written or mental computation. These situations provide opportunities for students to practice estimating reasonable results and then carrying out the calculation with a calculator.

For example, students could work to find the total of a class book order. Pose some questions to help them estimate first:

Will the total be over $50? between $50 and $100? between $100 and $150?

Help them to think about grouping the books to estimate:

How many of the books cost close to $1.00 each?

Then students can carry out the complete calculation with a calculator.

Ask questions to help students learn good practices with the calculator:

How are you keeping track of which books you have added and which you still need to add?

Is your result reasonable according to your estimate?

How can you double-check the calculator result (for example, by subtracting off each book)?

Students enjoy using what they perceive as an adult tool. Investigating with the calculator gives students an opportunity to notice mathematical patterns and to ask questions about mathematical symbols. For example, in a second-grade class, students were dividing lots of numbers by 2, which led to a discussion of the meaning of 0.5. In a fourth-grade class, some students became intrigued with the square root sign. The teacher challenged them to systematically keep track of the results of applying the square root symbol to whole numbers, starting with 1, and to come up with an idea about its meaning.

The calculator is an efficient tool for many purposes in life, and students should learn to use it sensibly, knowing that using it well depends on the user's correct analysis and organization of the problem, comparing its results with reasonable estimates, and double-checking.

Introducing and Managing the *LogoPaths* Software in Grade 4

LogoPaths Software is provided as a component of the *Investigations* curriculum. While using this software is optional, we recommend its use if you have computers either in your classroom or in your school's computer lab. The *Software Support Reference Guide* provides a complete description of the software and instructions for using the software activities.

In Grade 4, the *LogoPaths* Software is formally introduced in Unit 4, *Size, Shape, and Symmetry.* However, if you can give students some experience with the software early in the year, *before* Unit 4, they will be better prepared to use it to solve the specific problems in that unit.

Therefore, we recommend that you start using the software outside of math time starting with Unit 2, *Describing the Shape of the Data,* by reviewing *Feed the Turtle*—a game students played in Grade 3, with basic commands involving forward and backward steps in multiples of 10 and turns in multiples of 30°—and using the *Free Explore* option to experiment with drawing figures with different numbers of sides and a variety of side lengths and angle sizes.

In Unit 4, you will find suggestions for introducing the *LogoPaths* games and activities during specific sessions and integrating them into your Math Workshops. The software activities extend and deepen the mathematical ideas that are emphasized in this curriculum unit. In some cases, they allow students to work with geometric figures and with angles in ways that are not possible in the noncomputer activities.

Options for Introducing the *LogoPaths* Software

- *Computer lab:* If you have a computer laboratory with one computer for each pair of students, the entire class can become familiar with the computer activities at the same time. In this case, you will not need to devote time during math class to introduce the new software activity. Once an activity has been introduced, students can do it either during Math Workshop (if you have classroom computers) or during their scheduled lab time.

- *Large projection screen:* If you have a large projection screen, you can introduce the software activities to the whole class during a math session, immediately before Math Workshop or at another time of the day.

- *Small groups of students:* With fewer classroom computers, you can introduce the activities to small groups either before or during Math Workshop. These students can then be paired and become peer "teachers" of the software.

Regardless of the number of computers available, students generally benefit from working on these activities in pairs. This not only maximizes computer resources but also encourages students to consult, monitor, and teach one another. Generally, more than two students at one computer find it difficult to share. You may need to monitor computer use more closely than the other Math Workshop choices to ensure that all students get sufficient computer time. Each pair should spend at least 15–20 minutes at the computer for each activity.

Managing the Computer Environment

Students should be using the *LogoPaths* Software consistently throughout the school year. If you have daily access to a computer lab, you might take advantage of this to supplement your regular math class. If your school has a computer teacher, you might collaborate with that teacher to have students work on *LogoPaths* activities during some of their scheduled lab time.

More typically, a classroom will have a small number of computers. With computers in the classroom, pairs of students can cycle through the software activities during Math Workshop, just as they cycle through the other choices. Three to five classroom computers are ideal, but even with only one or two, students can have a successful computer experience. When you have fewer computers, find additional computer time for students throughout the day, outside of math.

Using *LogoPaths* All Year

Each unit includes a Technology Note with suggestions and reminders for ongoing use of the software during the rest of the year. Continued experience with *LogoPaths* allows students to become increasingly fluent in the mechanics of the software itself and able to better focus on the mathematical ideas of the game and activities.

Throughout Grade 4, the Resource Masters include some designed for continued student work with activities such as *Missing Measures* and *600 (800, 720, 920) Steps.* Students should also continue to play the games *Feed the Turtle* and *Mazes,* which help develop an understanding of paths and turning angles. The *Free Explore* activities offer experiences with the properties of two-dimensional (2-D) shapes, including their angles.

Students will continue to build on their knowledge and experiences with the *LogoPaths* Software in Grade 5.

Introducing the *LogoPaths* Activities

In your first introduction of the *Missing Measures* activity, show students the following:

- How to open *Free Explore* by clicking on it once
- How to enter forward and backward commands of any amount in the Command Center (e.g., **fd 82** or **bk 125**) (Note that move and turn inputs must be between –999 and 999.)
- How to enter right and left turn commands in multiples of 30° (e.g., **rt 90**, **rt 120**, **lt 30**, or **lt 150**)
- How to use the *Label Lengths* and *Label Turns* tools
- How to use the **ht** (hide turtle) and **st** (show turtle) commands

In your first introduction of the *600 (800) Steps* activity, show students the following:

- How to open *Free Explore* by clicking on it once
- How to enter forward and backward commands of any amount in the Command Center (e.g., **fd 82** or **bk 125**)
- How to use the *Label Lengths* and *Label Turns* tools
- How to use the **ht** (hide turtle) and **st** (show turtle) commands
- How to use the *Teach Tool* to make a procedure out of a set of commands and give it a name

In your first introduction of the *Mazes* game, show students the following:

- How to open *Mazes* by clicking on it once
- How to select the level they wish to play
- How to enter right and left turn commands with any number of degrees as input (e.g., **rt 50** or **lt 114**)
- How to use the *Turtle Turner* and the *Ruler* tool

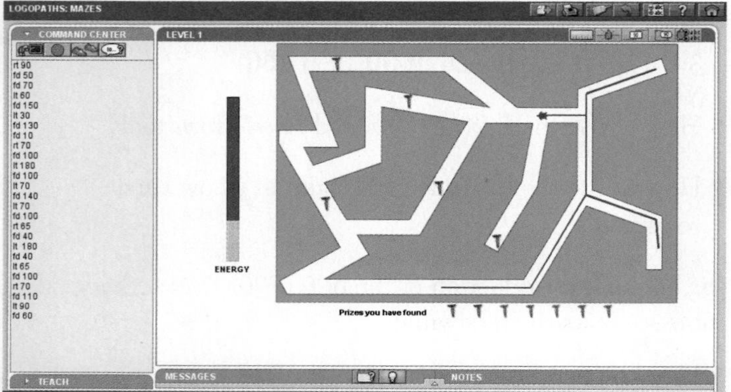

You can introduce more of the tools available in *LogoPaths* as students indicate interest and the need to use them.

- Students can use the penup (**pu**) and pendown (**pd**) commands to tell the turtle to draw as it moves. Type **pu** in the Command Center to move without drawing. Type **pd** for the turtle to draw as it moves.
- The repeat command tells the turtle to repeat a set of commands a specified number of times. The first input is the number of times to repeat, and the second is a list of commands enclosed in square brackets. For example, to repeat a forward move and a right turn three times, students might type **repeat 3 [fd 100 rt 90]**.
- Students can change the color, shape, and size of the turtle and the line it draws using the turtle features panel. Other features of how the turtle works (e.g., its speed) can be changed in the preferences panel.
- Further information about commands, tools, and buttons can be found in the online help.

It is likely that many students will discover other tools and their uses on their own as they spend more time working with the software. Encourage them to share their discoveries with one another.

Saving Student Work

If you want to discuss students' work later, they should either print it (if your computers are connected to a printer) or save their work on a disk. For information about printing or saving to a disk, see the *Software Support Reference Guide* contained in your curriculum guide package.

PART 6

Professional Development

Teacher Notes in *Investigations*

Teacher Notes are one of the most important professional development tools in *Investigations*. Each curriculum unit contains a collection of Teacher Notes that offer information about the mathematical content of that unit and how students learn it.

In this section of *Implementing Investigations in Grade 4,* you will find a set of Teacher Notes that addresses topics and issues applicable to the curriculum as a whole rather than to specific curriculum units.

These Teacher Notes provide important background about approaches to mathematics teaching and learning, about critical features of the mathematics classroom, and about how to develop an inclusive mathematics community in which all students participate. You can benefit from reading these notes, either individually or as the basis for discussion in teacher study groups, before starting to use the curriculum. Alternatively, you can read these notes gradually throughout the year while you are using the curriculum in your classroom. These brief essays take on new resonance and meaning as you have more experience with student learning and the *Investigations* curriculum. Plan to return to this collection periodically to review the ideas and reflect on the implications for classroom practice.

A complete list of the Teacher Note titles from each of the nine curriculum units is included on pages 66–67.

Computational Fluency and Place Value

Computational fluency includes accuracy, flexibility, and efficiency. When fluency with a particular operation is achieved, students can look at the problem as a whole, choose a solution strategy that they can carry out easily without becoming bogged down or losing track of their steps, use their strategy to solve the problem accurately, recognize whether the result is reasonable, and double-check their work. Students who are fluent have a repertoire that includes mental strategies, strategies in which only intermediate steps are jotted down while other steps are carried out mentally, and strategies that require a complete written solution. They are flexible in their choice of algorithm or procedure, and they can use one method to check another.

Developing computational fluency with whole numbers is central to the elementary curriculum. This development includes the building blocks of computation:

- Understanding the base-ten number system and its place value notation
- Understanding the meaning of the operations and their relationships
- Knowing the basic addition and multiplication number combinations (the "facts") and their counterparts for subtraction and division
- Estimating reasonable results
- Interpreting problems embedded in contexts and applying the operations correctly to these problems
- Learning, practicing, and consolidating accurate and efficient strategies for computing
- Developing curiosity about numbers and operations, their characteristics, and how they work
- Learning to articulate, represent, and justify generalizations

At each grade level, computational fluency looks different. Students are progressing in learning the meaning of the four arithmetic operations with whole numbers, developing methods grounded in this meaning, and gradually solving problems of greater difficulty through the grades. At each grade level, benchmarks for whole number computation indicate what is expected of all students by the end of each curriculum unit and each grade, although work at each grade level goes beyond these benchmarks. Gradually, approaches to problems become more efficient, flexible, and accurate. For example, in Grade 1, many students begin the year adding by direct modeling of the problem with objects and counting the sum by ones. By the end of the year, students are expected to start with one of the quantities and count on the other, and for some combinations students "just know" the sum or use known combinations to solve others ("I know $4 + 4 = 8$, so $4 + 5 = 9$"). In Grade 4, many students start the year solving some multiplication problems by skip counting, but by the end of the year, they are expected to solve multidigit multiplication problems such as 34×68 by breaking problems into subproblems, based on the distributive property.

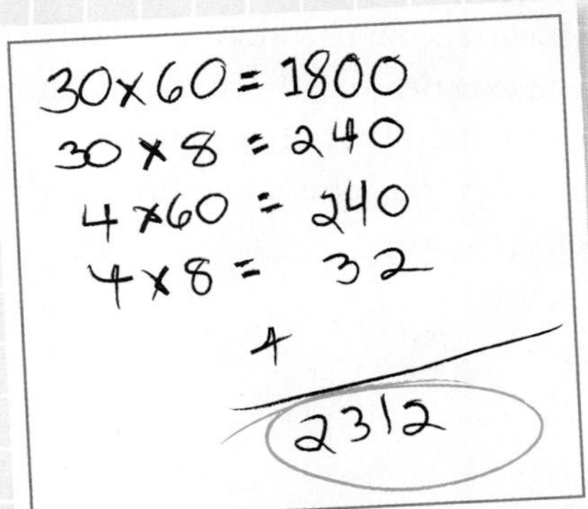

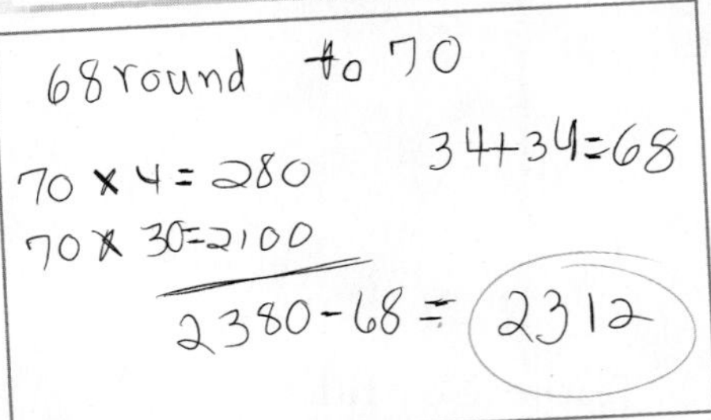

Sample Student Work

Understanding the Base-Ten Number System

Learning about whole number computation is closely connected to learning about the base-ten number system. The base-ten number system is a "place value" system. That is, any numeral, say 2, can represent different values, depending on where it appears in a written number: it can represent 2 ones, 2 tens, 2 hundreds, 2 thousands, as well as 2 tenths, 2 hundredths, and so forth. Understanding this place value system requires coordinating the way we write the numerals that represent a particular number (e.g., 217) and the way we name numbers in words (e.g., two hundred seventeen) with how those symbols represent quantities.

The heart of this work is relating written numerals to the quantity and to how the quantity is composed. It builds from work on tens and ones in Grades 1 and 2 to a focus on numbers in the hundreds and thousands in Grade 3, and work with numbers in the ten thousands, hundred thousands, and beyond in Grades 4 and 5. Knowing place value is not simply a matter of saying that 217 "has 2 hundreds, 1 ten, and 7 ones," which students can easily learn to do by following a pattern without attaching much meaning to what they are saying. Students must learn to visualize how 217 is built up from hundreds, tens, and ones, in a way that helps them relate its value to other quantities. Understanding the place value of a number such as 217 entails knowing, for example, that 217 is closer to 200 than to 300, that it is 100 more than 117, that it is 17 more than 200, that it is 3 less than 220, and that it is composed of 21 tens and 7 ones.

A thorough understanding of the base-ten number system is one of the critical building blocks for developing computational fluency. Understanding place value is at the heart of estimating and computing. For example, consider adding two different quantities to 32:

$32 + 30 =$ _____

$32 + 3 =$ _____

How much will 32 increase in each case? Students think about how the first sum will now have 6 tens, but the ones will not change, whereas in the second sum, the ones will change, but the tens remain the same. Adding three *tens* almost doubles 32, while adding three *ones* increases its value by a small amount. Considering the place value of numbers that are being added, subtracted, multiplied, or divided provides the basis for developing a reasonable estimate of the result.

The composition of numbers from multiples of 1, 10, 100, 1,000, and so forth, is the basis for most of the strategies students adopt for whole number operations. Students' computational algorithms and procedures depend on knowing how to decompose numbers and knowing the effects of operating with multiples of 10. For example, one of the most common algorithms for addition is adding by place. Each number is decomposed into ones, tens, hundreds, and so forth; these parts are then combined. For example,

$326 + 493$

$300 + 400 = 700$

$20 + 90 = 110$

$6 + 3 = 9$

$700 + 110 + 9 = 819$

To carry out this algorithm fluently, students must know a great deal about place value, not just how to decompose numbers. They must also be able to apply their knowledge of single-digit sums such as $3 + 4$ and $2 + 9$ to sums such as $300 + 400$ and $20 + 90$. In other words, they know how to interpret the place value of numbers *as they operate with them*—in this case, that just as 2 ones plus 9 ones equals 11 ones, 2 tens plus 9 tens equals 11 tens, or 110.

As with addition, algorithms for multidigit multiplication also depend on knowing how the place value of numbers is interpreted as numbers are multiplied. Again, students must understand how they can apply knowledge of single-digit combinations such as 3×4 to solve problems such as 36×42.

For example,

36×42

$30 \times 40 = 1{,}200$

$30 \times 2 = 60$

$6 \times 40 = 240$

$6 \times 2 = 12$

$1{,}200 + 240 + 60 + 12 = 1{,}512$

Students gradually learn how a knowledge of 3×4 helps them solve 30×4, 3×40, 30×40, 3×400, and so forth.

Building Computational Fluency Over Time

There is a tremendous amount of work to do in the area of numbers and operations in Grades K–5.

- Kindergartners and first graders are still working on coordinating written and spoken numbers with their quantitative meaning.
- Second graders are uncovering the relationship between 10 ones and 1 ten and between 10 tens and 1 hundred.
- Third graders are immersed in how the properties of multiplication differ from the properties of addition.
- Fourth and fifth graders are solving multidigit problems and becoming flexible in their use of a number of algorithms.

This list provides only a brief glimpse of how much work there is to do in these grades.

Students gain computational fluency in each operation through several years of careful development. Extended time across several grades is spent on each operation. Students build computational fluency with small numbers as they learn about the meaning and properties of the operation. Then they gradually expand their work to more difficult problems as they develop, analyze, compare, and practice general methods.

Let's use subtraction as an example of this process:

- In Kindergarten and Grade 1, students solve subtraction problems by modeling the action of subtraction.
- By Grade 2, students are articulating and using the inverse relationship between addition and subtraction to solve problems like the following: "If I have 10 cookies, how many more cookies do I need to bake so I have 24?"
- During Grades 2 and 3, students become fluent with the subtraction "facts" and model and solve a variety of types of subtraction problems, including comparison and missing part problems. By Grade 3, as students' understanding of the base-ten number system grows, they use their understanding of place value to solve problems with larger numbers.
- In Grades 3 and 4, students articulate, represent, and justify important generalizations about subtraction. For example, if you add the same amount to (or subtract it from) each number in a subtraction expression, the difference does not change, as in the equation $483 - 197 = 486 - 200$. In these grades, students also choose one or two procedures, practice them, and expand their command of these procedures with multidigit numbers.
- In Grades 4 and 5, as their fluency with subtraction increases, students analyze and compare strategies for solving subtraction problems. Because they are fluent with more "transparent" algorithms for subtraction in which the place value of the numbers is clear, they are now in a position to appreciate the shortcut notation of the U.S. traditional regrouping algorithm for subtraction, analyze how it works, and compare it to other algorithms. (See the Teacher Note, Computational Algorithms and Methods.)

This account gives only a glimpse of the work involved in understanding subtraction across the grades. Each operation has a similar complexity. It is critical that the time and depth required for the careful development of ideas is devoted to this strand. For this reason, in each of Grades 1–4, there are four units spread throughout the year that focus on whole numbers, operations, and the base-ten number system. In Kindergarten, three units focus on counting, quantity, and modeling addition and subtraction. In Grade 5, because of the increased emphasis on rational numbers, three units focus on whole numbers and two units focus on fractions, decimals, and percents. The whole number units within each grade build on each other in a careful sequence.

As you work with your students on whole number computation, here are some questions to keep in mind as you assess their progress toward computational fluency [adapted from Russell, 2000, p. 158]:

- Do students know and draw on basic facts and other number relationships?
- Do students use and understand the structure of the base-ten number system? For example, do students know the result of adding 100 to 2,340 or multiplying 40×500?
- Do students recognize related problems that can help with the problem?
- Do students use relationships among operations?
- Do students know what each number and numeral in the problem means (including subproblems)?
- Can students explain why the steps being used actually work?
- Do students have a clear way to record and keep track of their procedures?
- Do students have more than one approach for solving problems in each operation? Can they determine which problems lend themselves to different methods?

Supporting Computational Fluency Across the Curriculum

Work in the other content areas also connects to and supports the work on computational fluency in the number and operations units. For example, an emphasis on the foundations of algebra across the grades opens up important opportunities to strengthen work with numbers and operations. Within the number and operations units themselves, articulation, representation, and justification of general claims about the operations (an aspect of early algebraic thinking) strengthen students' understanding of the operations (see the Teacher Note, Foundations of Algebra in the Elementary Grades, and the Algebra Connections essay in each of the number and operations units). The work with functions provides interesting problem contexts in which students' work on ratio and on constant rates of change connect to and support their work on multiplication (see the Teacher Note, Foundations of Algebra in the Elementary Grades, and the Algebra Connections essay in each of the patterns, functions, and change units). Geometry and measurement units also provide contexts in which students revisit multiplication. Finally, the Classroom Routines (in Grades K–3) and Ten-Minute Math (in Grades 3–5) provide ongoing, regular practice of estimation and computation.

Reference

Russell, S. J. (2000). Developing computational fluency with whole numbers. *Teaching Children Mathematics 7*, 154–158.

Teacher Note

Computational Algorithms and Methods

In the elementary grades, a central part of students' work is learning about addition, subtraction, multiplication, and division and becoming fluent and flexible in solving whole number computation problems. In the *Investigations* curriculum, students use methods and algorithms in which they can see clearly the steps of their solution and focus on the mathematical sense of what they are doing. They use and compare several different methods to deepen their understanding of the properties of the operations and to develop flexibility in solving problems. They practice methods for each operation so that they can use them efficiently to solve problems.

What Is an Algorithm?

An algorithm is a series of well-defined steps used to solve a certain class of problem (for example, all addition problems). Often, the sequence of steps is repeated with successive parts of the problem. For example, here is an example of an addition algorithm:

$249 + 674$

$200 + 600 = 800$

$40 + 70 = 110$

$9 + 4 = 13$

$800 + 110 + 13 = 923$

Written instructions for this algorithm might begin as follows:

1. Find the left-most place represented in the addends and add all the amounts in that place.
2. Move one place to the right and add all the amounts in that place in all the addends.
3. Repeat step 2 until all parts of all addends have been added.
4. Add the sums of each place.

To specify these instructions, as if we were going to teach them to a computer, we would have more work to do to make them even more specific and precise. For example, how is step 4 carried out? Should each place be added separately again and then combined? In practice, when students and adults use this algorithm, the partial sums that must be added in step 4 are generally easy enough to add mentally, as they are in this problem, although occasionally one might again break up some of the numbers.

Algorithms like this one, once understood and practiced, are general methods that can be used for a whole class of problems. The adding by place algorithm, for example, can be generalized for use with any addition problem. As students' knowledge of the number system expands, they learn to apply this algorithm to, for example, larger numbers or to decimals. Students also learn how to use clear and concise notation, to carry out some steps mentally, and to record those intermediate steps needed so that they can keep track of the solution process.

Nonalgorithmic Methods for Computing with Whole Numbers

Students also learn methods for computing with whole numbers that are not algorithmic—that is, one cannot completely specify the steps for carrying them out, and they do not generally involve a repetition of steps. However, these methods are studied because they are useful for solving certain problems. In thinking through why and how they work, students also deepen their understanding of the properties of the various operations. This work provides opportunities for students to articulate generalizations about the operations and to represent and justify them.

For example, here is one method a third grader might use to solve this problem:

$7.46 + $3.28 = $7.50 + $3.24 = $10.74

The student changed the addition expression to an equivalent expression with numbers that made it easier to find the sum mentally. First graders often use this idea as they learn some of their addition combinations, transforming a combination they are learning into an equivalent combination they already know: $7 + 5 = 6 + 6 = 12$.

When students try to use the same method to make a subtraction problem easier to solve, they find that they must modify their method to create an equivalent problem. Instead of adding an amount to one number and subtracting it from the other, as in addition, they must add the same amount to (or subtract it from) each number:

$182 - 69 = 183 - 70 = 113$

Throughout the *Investigations* curriculum, methods like these are introduced and studied to deepen students' understanding of how these operations work and to engage them in proving their ideas using representations of the operations.

Because the ways in which a problem might be changed to make an equivalent problem that is easier to solve can vary (although it might be possible to precisely specify a particular variant of one of these methods), these methods are not algorithms. Students do not generally use such methods to solve a whole class of problems (e.g., any addition problem); rather, students who are flexible in their understanding of numbers and operations use finding equivalent expressions as one possible method and notice when a problem lends itself to solving in this way.

Learning Algorithms Across the Grades

In *Investigations,* students develop, use, and compare algorithms and other methods. These are not "invented" but are constructed with teacher support, as students' understanding of the operations and the base-ten number system grow (see the Teacher Note, Computational Fluency and Place Value). Because the algorithms that students learn are so grounded in knowledge of the operation and the number system, most of them arise naturally as students progress from single-digit to multidigit problems. For example, the adding by place addition algorithm shown earlier naturally grows out of what students are learning about how a number such as 24 is composed of 2 tens and 4 ones. It is part of the teacher's role to make these methods explicit, help students understand and practice them, and support students to gradually use more efficient methods. For example, a second grader who is adding on one number in parts might solve $49 + 34$ by adding on 10, then another 10, then another 10, then 4 to 49 ($49 + 10 + 10 + 10 + 4$). By having this student compare solutions with another student's whose first step is $49 + 30$, the teacher helps the first student analyze what is the same and different about their solutions and opens up the possibility for the first student of a more efficient method—adding on a multiple of 10 all at once rather than breaking it into 10s.

The algorithms and other methods that students learn about and use in *Investigations* for multidigit problems are characterized by their *transparency.* Transparent algorithms

- make the properties of the operations visible.
- show the place value of the numbers in the problem.
- make clear how a problem is broken into subproblems and how the results of these subproblems are recombined.

These characteristics are critical for students while they are learning the meaning of the operations and are building their understanding of the base-ten system. Here is an example of a transparent multiplication algorithm that might be used by a fourth grader:

$$\begin{array}{r} 34 \\ \times\ 78 \\ \hline 2100 \\ 280 \\ 240 \\ 32 \\ \hline \end{array}$$

$$2{,}000 + 500 + 150 + 2 = 2{,}652$$

In this algorithm, students record all numbers fully, showing the place value of all the digits. Because the result of each multiplication is shown, the application of the distributive property is kept track of clearly.

There is a misperception that many different algorithms might arise in a single classroom and that this multitude of algorithms will be confusing. In fact, there are only a few basic algorithms and methods for each operation that arise from students' work and that are emphasized in the curriculum. Each is tied closely to how students solve problems and to the basic characteristics and properties of the operation. Teacher Notes throughout the curriculum provide more detail about these methods.

Students can and do develop efficiency and fluency with these more transparent algorithms. As they do, they do some steps mentally and may no longer need to write out every step to keep track of their work. For example, in using the adding by place algorithm to add 249 + 674, a competent user might simply jot down 800, 110, 13, and then add those partial sums mentally and record the answer. There may be times when you require students to write out their complete solution method so that you can see how they are solving problems, but for everyday use, efficient users of such algorithms will record only the steps they need.

These algorithms and methods are studied, compared, and analyzed for different reasons. All of them are transparent, preserve place value, and make visible important properties such as distributivity. Some can be practiced and provide general, efficient methods. Others are useful only for particular problems but are studied because of what they illuminate about the operations.

Studying the U.S. Standard Algorithms

The U.S. standard algorithms for addition, subtraction, and multiplication are also explicitly studied in *Investigations* but only after students are fully grounded in understanding the operation and using transparent algorithms for multidigit computation. These algorithms were developed for efficiency and compactness for handwritten computation. When these algorithms are used as a primary teaching tool, their very compactness, which can be an advantage for experienced users, becomes a disadvantage for young learners because they obscure the place value of the numbers and the properties of the operation.

Some students do use the standard algorithms with understanding. As these algorithms come up in class, they should be incorporated into the list of class strategies. Teachers should make sure that students who use them understand what the shortcut notation represents and that they can explain why these algorithms make sense. They should also know and understand other methods. In Grade 4, students revisit the U.S. standard addition algorithm formally, analyze how and why it works, and compare it to other algorithms they are using. In Grade 5, students revisit the U.S. standard subtraction and multiplication algorithms in the same way. Division methods studied in this curriculum focus on the inverse relationship between multiplication and division.

Teacher Note

Representations and Contexts for Mathematical Work

Mathematics involves describing and analyzing all kinds of mathematical relationships. Throughout the *Investigations* curriculum, students use representations and contexts to help them visualize these mathematical relationships. Thinking with representations and contexts allows students to express and further develop their ideas and enables students to engage with each other's ideas. Whether solving a multiplication problem, finding the area of a rectangle, describing the relationship between two variables, or ordering fractions, students use representations and contexts to investigate and explain.

The *Investigations* curriculum introduces a limited number of carefully chosen representations and contexts because they provide representations of mathematical relationships that students can use to solve problems and/or to show their ideas and solutions to others. Students may first use representations or contexts concretely, drawing or modeling with materials. Later, they incorporate these representations and contexts into mental models that they can call on to visualize the structure of problems and their solutions. Students develop the habit of making drawings, building models, and using representations to think with and to explain their thinking to others. They develop a repertoire of representations that they know well and can apply when faced with unfamiliar problem situations.

Good contexts and representations have the following characteristics:

- They are useful for a whole class of problems (e.g., addition problems).
- They can be extended to accommodate more complex problems and/or students' expanding repertoire of numbers.
- They do not overwhelm or interfere with the focus on mathematical content.
- Their structure embodies important characteristics of the mathematical relationships.

This Teacher Note provides some examples of how models, materials, and contexts are used by students across the grades.

Representations

Basic representations in the *Investigations* curriculum include connecting cubes, the 100 chart (and its variants, the 300, 1,000, and 10,000 charts), number lines, arrays, and sets of two-dimensional (2-D) and three-dimensional (3-D) shapes. Each representation provides access to certain characteristics, actions, and properties of numbers and operations or of geometric properties and relationships. Here are two examples.

Connecting Cubes

Connecting cubes are a basic material for counting and for modeling addition and subtraction in Grades K–2. The cubes are a discrete model of whole numbers and provide a uniform counting material for representing ones. Because they connect, they can be organized into sticks of ten cubes so that students can use them to represent tens and ones.

The individual cubes are visible in the connected stick of ten, so students can visualize how this stick represents the equivalence of 1 ten and 10 ones and then how 10 ten-sticks is equivalent to 1 hundred and 100 ones. Connecting cubes are a flexible material. They are well suited for modeling the basic actions of joining and separating. They can also be used to construct rectangular arrays for studying multiplication and area. Students also use the cubes to construct rectangular prisms and to analyze and visualize how the volume of the shape consists of a certain number of layers, each of which has the same dimensions.

Each layer is 3 × 4. There are six layers.

The Number Line

The number line is another key representation of numbers. This continuous representation offers students another view of the number sequence and number relationships. Students' beginning work with number lines involves number lines that are already marked with the counting numbers.

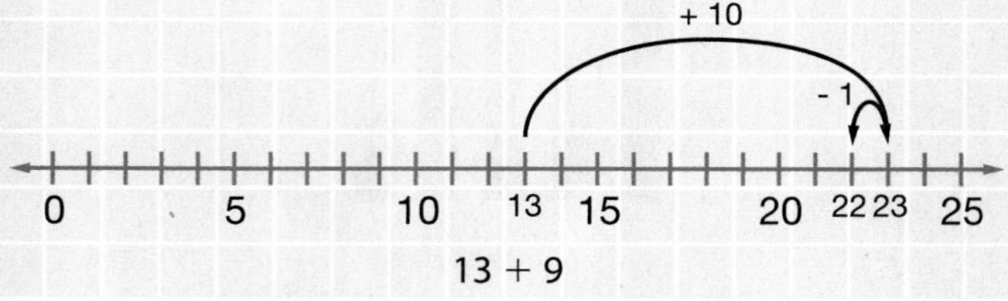

I jumped up 10 to 23, then back 1.

Later, students choose the part of the number line they need and which points on it should be marked as they use it to solve problems.

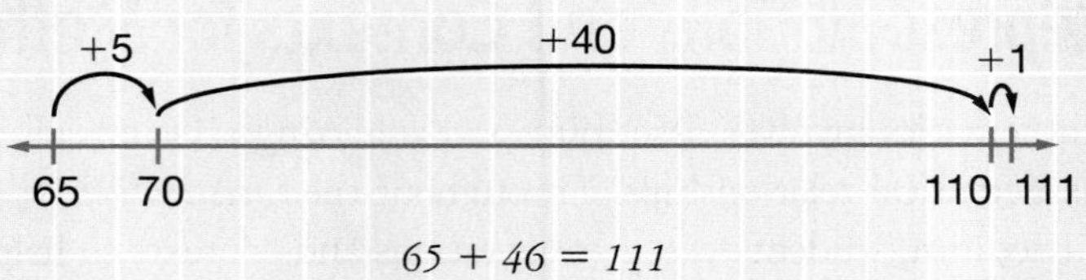

65 + 46 = 111

The number line provides access to the idea that numbers are infinite. At first, students come to this idea in relation to the counting sequence of whole numbers. Later, as they encounter negative numbers, they consider how the number line extends in both directions, that both positive and negative numbers "go on forever." In their study of rational numbers, they use the number line to model fractions and decimal fractions and consider how the segments of the number line between two successive whole numbers can be divided into smaller and smaller pieces. In later years, they will come to understand that there are an infinite number of numbers between any two successive integers.

For students to use a representation well, they need enough experience with it so that they understand its basic characteristics and can then use it themselves to model and solve problems. For example, using an unmarked number line flexibly requires that students have enough prior experience using the marked number line to count, add, and subtract.

Using Different Representations

Different representations offer different models of the mathematics and access to different mathematical ideas. For example, both place value models and number lines are useful in students' study of subtraction, but they each allow students to see different aspects of subtraction. A student solving the problem 103 − 37 might think about subtracting 37 in parts by visualizing a place value model of the numbers, subtracting 3 tens and then 7 ones (which, for ease of subtraction from 103, the student might split into 3 + 4).

Another student might think about creating an easier, equivalent problem: 103 − 37 = 106 − 40. This student might visualize "sliding" the interval from 37 to 103 along a number line to determine how to change the numbers, while preserving the difference between them.

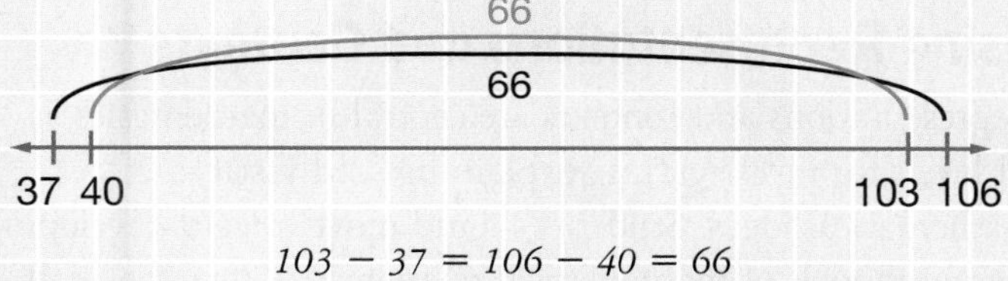

More details about these and other representations are provided throughout the curriculum units.

Contexts

Contexts and stories are also used to represent mathematical relationships. A good context can be created from familiar events or fantasy. Contexts that students can imagine and visualize give them access to ways of thinking about the mathematical ideas and relationships they are studying. For a context to be useful, it must be connected enough to students' experience that students can imagine and represent the actions and relationships. At the same time, the details of the context need not be elaborate, so that the nonmathematical aspects of the context stay in the background. Here are two examples.

The Penny Jar

One of the contexts in the patterns and functions units in Grades 1 and 4 is the Penny Jar. The Penny Jar contains some number of pennies (the starting amount) and then has a certain number of pennies added to it each day or with each round (the constant rate of change). This is one of the contexts used to engage students in exploring a function—the relationship of the number of days to the total number of pennies—that involves a constant rate of change. Students' knowledge of similar real-world contexts engages students quickly in the mathematics and helps them visualize the mathematical relationships, but it is not so elaborate that it obscures or distracts from the mathematics.

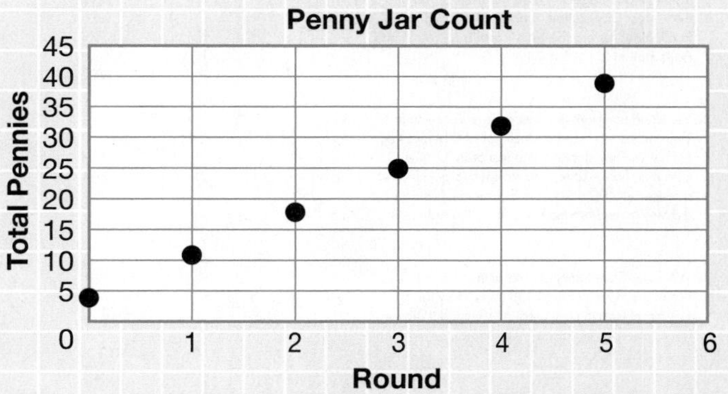

Number of Rounds	Total Number of Pennies
Start	4
1	11
2	18
3	25
4	32
5	39

Once students are familiar with the Penny Jar context, they can represent it in multiple ways, using pictures, tables, and graphs, to describe and analyze the relationship between the two variables.

Travel Stories

In Grade 3, travel stories are used as a context for subtraction. Students are familiar with taking trips by car or bus or have encountered such trips in stories or movies. They know about a trip having a starting point, an ending point, and a certain distance traveled. They are also familiar with stopping along the way for a meal or to take a break and with discussing how much of the distance has been covered and how much is still ahead of them.

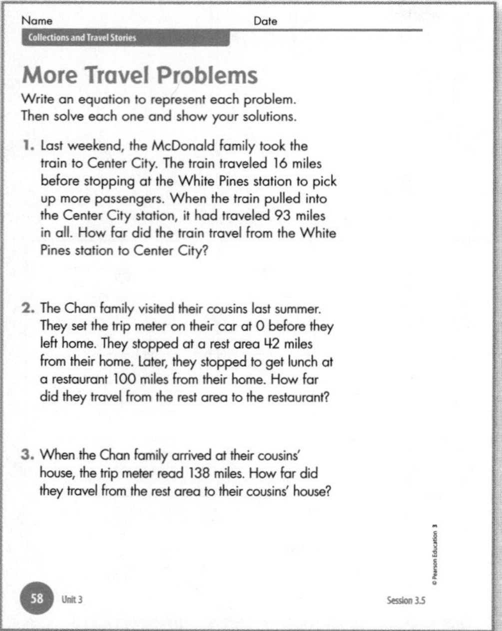

Name Date

Collections and Travel Stories

More Travel Problems

Write an equation to represent each problem.
Then solve each one and show your solutions.

1. Last weekend, the McDonald family took the train to Center City. The train traveled 16 miles before stopping at the White Pines station to pick up more passengers. When the train pulled into the Center City station, it had traveled 93 miles in all. How far did the train travel from the White Pines station to Center City?

2. The Chan family visited their cousins last summer. They set the trip meter on their car at 0 before they left home. They stopped at a rest area 42 miles from their home. Later, they stopped to get lunch at a restaurant 100 miles from their home. How far did they travel from the rest area to the restaurant?

3. When the Chan family arrived at their cousins' house, the trip meter read 138 miles. How far did they travel from the rest area to their cousins' house?

© Pearson Education 3

58 Unit 3 Session 3.5

▲ **Grade 3 Unit 3 *Student Activity Book*, page 58**

Helping Students Connect to Contexts

Teachers often personalize these contexts for students to help them visualize and use it. For example, when using the Penny Jar context, one first-grade teacher had a brief discussion about places they or someone else they know used to hold money and some reasons that money might get added to any of these. The teacher then referred to some of these situations as they discussed problems, "Let's say we're talking about Andre's situation when he is doing his chores. He has 3 pennies in the jar, and he is going to put in 2 pennies for each chore he completes." In using the travel story context, teachers also refer to situations that are familiar to students: "So let's say Janelle and her family are setting off to visit her grandma, like they did last summer, and the whole trip is 274 miles. …"

More details about these and other contexts are provided throughout the curriculum units.

Using Representations and Contexts

Representations and contexts are central in mathematics at all levels for investigating, explaining, and justifying mathematical ideas. Students should move toward developing mental models of mathematical relationships that they call on routinely and will often use pictures, diagrams, and objects when they encounter new kinds of problems.

Students should use representations and contexts judiciously and with purpose. A first grader who is solving word problems that involve addition and subtraction might model every problem with cubes. Another student in the same class might model one or two problems; then, having visually confirmed the action of the operation, the student might solve the rest by imagining one quantity and counting on. A third student—or the same student later in the year—might reason about the numbers without using an image or model. In class discussions, both the teacher and students use representations to clarify and investigate mathematical ideas and to help all students focus on what is being discussed.

As a teacher, one of your roles is to support students in using representations and contexts and to help them develop mental images that they can call on. On the one hand, students need not show a picture for a problem when they have developed more efficient numerical tools and methods. For example, when one fourth grader was asked to solve a multiplication problem in two ways, he solved the problem by breaking it up efficiently, using the distributive property, and then showed a solution using groups of tally marks. His teacher let him know that using tally marks was not what she was looking for from him and reminded him of the work the class had been doing on changing one of the numbers in the problem and then adjusting the product.

On the other hand, students should understand that the use of representations and models is not a "crutch" in mathematics but is a powerful set of tools for investigating problem situations. In the classroom, encourage representation as a central part of mathematics activity. Make a habit of asking questions such as these:

- Is there a way you can show us your thinking using the number line or the 100 chart?
- Can you explain how your strategy makes sense using the travel context we have been using for some of the problems?
- You used a number line and Chris used a place-value sketch showing tens and ones. What is similar or different about these two approaches? Where can you see the four tens in Chris's place value sketch on Luc's number line solution?
- Karen, you are thinking of the multiplication problem as representing 47 classrooms with 23 students in each class. How did this context help you keep track of the parts of the problem?
- Can you show us with a picture or on the Geoboard what you mean when you say "a triangle is half of a rectangle"?
- What if you needed to explain or prove what you are saying to someone who came to visit our classroom? Is there a way you can show me why what you are saying is true with a picture or diagram?

When students are accustomed to incorporating representations in their daily mathematics work and considering what representations can be helpful for explaining mathematical ideas, they can also create their own images appropriate to a particular problem situation. Help students make these images simple enough so that they serve the mathematics rather than obscure it. The use of representations in class discussions helps illuminate students' ideas for each other and, by putting out an image that is available to all students, clarifies what mathematical relationships are being considered and invites more students into the conversation.

For further examples of students' use of representations, see the classroom stories in the section "Language and Representation" in Part 7, Working with the Range of Learners: Classroom Cases.

Foundations of Algebra in the Elementary Grades

Algebra is a multifaceted area of mathematics content that has been described and classified in different ways. Across many of the classification schemes, four areas foundational to the study of algebra stand out: (1) generalizing and formalizing patterns; (2) representing and analyzing the structure of numbers and operations; (3) using symbolic notation to express functions and relations; and (4) representing and analyzing change.

In the *Investigations* curriculum, these areas of early algebra are addressed in two major ways: (1) work within the counting, number, and operations units focusing on generalizations that arise in the course of students' study of numbers and operations and (2) a coherent strand, consisting of one unit in each grade, K–5, that focuses on patterns, functions, and change. These two areas of emphasis are described here, followed by some additional information about the goals of work on early algebra in the curriculum.

Early Algebra: Making General Claims About Numbers and Operations

Each *Investigations* unit on counting, numbers, and operations includes a focus on reasoning and generalizing about numbers and operations. Even in beginning work with numbers and operations in Kindergarten and Grade 1, students are already noticing regularities about numbers and operations. For example, in the K–1 game *Double Compare,* each student in the pair selects two number cards. The student with the greater sum says "me." In this early work, before students know their single-digit addition combinations, most students are counting all or counting on to determine the sum. But consider how students are reasoning in the following brief episode:

> Bridget and Siva are playing *Double Compare.* Bridget draws a 5 and a 2; Siva draws a 5 and a 3 and immediately says "me," indicating that he has the greater sum. Siva usually counts both amounts by ones to get the sum, so the teacher asks him, "How did you know you have more?" Siva responds, "Because I have a 3 and she has a 2, and 3 is bigger." Bridget is nodding vigorously and adds, "The 5s don't count."

How are the students in this episode figuring out who has the greater sum? Why does Siva only compare 3 with 2, and what does Bridget mean when she says the "5s don't count"? Implicit in these students' work is a general claim about adding numbers that many young students use: If you are comparing two addition expressions, and one of the addends in the first expression is the same as one of the addends in the second, then you need only compare the other two addends to determine which expression has the greater sum. This is a mouthful to put into words, and students might not be able to articulate this idea completely; nevertheless, they are reasoning based on this idea. In later years, this idea can be represented with symbolic notation:

For any numbers a, b, c, and d when $a = c$ and $b < d$, then $a + b < c + d$.

$a = c$	$b < d$	$a + b < c + d$
$5 = 5$	$2 < 3$	$5 + 2 < 5 + 3$

Part of the teaching work in the elementary grades is to help students articulate, represent, investigate, and justify such general claims that arise naturally in the course of their work with numbers and operations. In each of the number and operations units in Grades K–5, the Algebra Connections essay highlights several of these general ideas about properties and relationships relevant to the work in that curriculum unit, with examples of how students think about and represent them. Investigation and discussion of some of these generalizations are built into unit sessions; for others, Algebra Notes alert the teacher to activities or discussions in which these ideas are likely to arise and could be pursued.

In the course of articulating, representing, and justifying their ideas about such general claims, students in the elementary grades are beginning to engage in proving—a central part of mathematics. They consider the questions: Does this generalization apply to *all* numbers (in the domain under consideration, usually whole numbers)? Why does it work? How do you know? In two of the number and operations units in each grade, 2–5, you will find a Teacher Note that focuses on proof and justification. These Teacher Notes provide examples of the ways that students at that grade level engage in proving and how their proofs, based on representations, are related to the proofs a mathematician might carry out.

Examples of the general claims highlighted in the curriculum in Grades K–2 are as follows:

- Counting the same set of objects in different orders results in the same count.
- If one number is larger than another, and the same number is added to each, the first total will be larger than the second: $3 + 5 > 2 + 5$.
- You can add two numbers in either order: $6 + 3 = 3 + 6$.
- If you add an amount to one addend and subtract it from another addend, the sum remains the same: $6 + 6 = 12$; $7 + 5 = 12$.
- Addition and subtraction are related. If adding two numbers gives a certain sum, then subtracting one of the addends from the sum results in the other addend: $6 + 7 = 13$; $13 - 7 = 6$; $13 - 6 = 7$.
- You can break numbers into parts to add them: $6 + 8 = 6 + (4 + 4) = (6 + 4) + 4$.
- If you add two even numbers, the sum is even. If you add two odd numbers, the sum is even. If you add an even number and an odd number, the sum is odd.

Some of the generalizations investigated in Grades K–2 are revisited in Grades 3–5 with higher numbers and more complex problems. In addition, new general claims are investigated. Examples of general claims highlighted in Grades 3–5 are as follows:

- If you add the same amount to both numbers in a subtraction problem, the difference does not change: $145 - 97 = 148 - 100$.
- You can multiply two numbers in either order: $32 \times 20 = 20 \times 32$.
- You can break numbers into parts to multiply them, but each part of each number must be multiplied by each part of the other number: $7 \times 24 = 7 \times (20 + 4) = (7 \times 20) + (7 \times 4)$.
- Multiplication and division are related. If multiplying two numbers gives a certain product, then dividing that product by one of the original factors results in the other factor: $9 \times 8 = 72$; $72 \div 8 = 9$; $72 \div 9 = 8$.
- A factor of a number is a factor of multiples of that number: 3 is a factor of 15; 15 is a factor of 30, so 3 is a factor of 30.
- If you double (or triple) one of the factors in a multiplication problem and halve (or third) the other, the product remains the same: $164 \times 4 = 328 \times 2$.

Early Algebra: Patterns, Functions, and Change

Investigations includes a coherent K–5 strand on patterns, functions, and change, with one unit in each grade. The content of these units starts with repeating patterns and number sequences in Grades K and 1, connects these patterns and sequences to functional relationships beginning in Grade 2, and then develops ideas about linear and nonlinear contexts that involve relationships between two variables in Grades 3–5. In each of these units in K–5, the Algebra Connections essay highlights some of the ideas students work on in that unit, and how they connect to later work in algebra.

Patterns and Functions in Grades K–2

Work with repeating patterns has long been a staple of mathematics work in the primary grades, but it often seems to have little connection to work in later grades. In the *Investigations* sequence, students' study of the structure of repeating patterns is connected to work with ratios and linear functions by associating the repeating pattern with the counting numbers. Consider this example:

> Students have been building repeating color patterns using connecting cubes. This red-blue-green repeating pattern has been numbered with the counting numbers, starting with 1. Students are considering which numbers are associated with the green cubes:
>
> 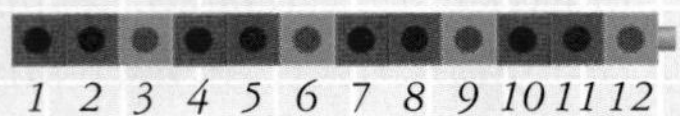
>
>
> Kamala says that the greens have a "counting by 3s" pattern: 3, 6, 9, 12. Esperanza says, "it will always be on the threes because every time you skip two, then it's green." Theo adds, remembering a previous Investigation in which they built buildings from connecting cubes with the same number of cubes in each layer: "It's like the same pattern we made when we made the building. It's always adding threes. One floor is three, two floors is six, and you keep adding three—3, 6, 9, um, 12, and you keep going by 3s."
>
> 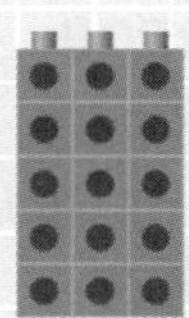

Students are recognizing the underlying 1:3 ratio in both situations. In the repeating pattern, there is a relationship between the position of each green cube among all green cubes and its position among all the cubes: the *first* green is in position 3 in the sequence, the *second* green in position 6, the *third* green in position 9, and so forth. In the cube building, there are 3 cubes for each floor: one floor has 3 cubes, 2 floors have 6 cubes, 3 floors have 9 cubes, and so forth. These constant ratio situations are students' first examples of linear change—change at a constant rate.

Examples of ideas investigated in Grades K–2 in these units are as follows:

- Repeating patterns can be described as iterations of a unit. This repeating color pattern can be divided into its units, the part that repeats:

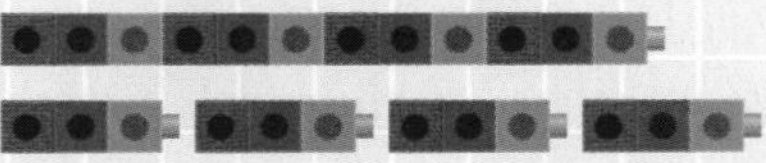

- When the elements of a repeating pattern are numbered with the counting numbers, elements in the pattern can be characterized by a particular number sequence. In a red-blue-red-blue connecting cube train, the blue cubes are numbered 2, 4, 6, 8, . . . , and the red cubes are numbered 1, 3, 5, 7, ...

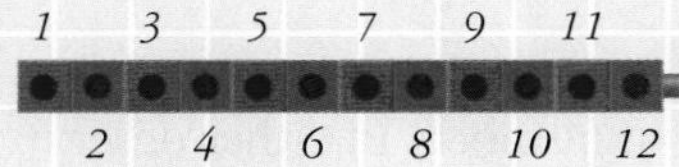

- The same number sequence can represent different situations. The blue cubes in a red-blue repeating pattern and the claps in a tap-clap repeating pattern fall in the same numbered positions.
- In a ratio situation, as one quantity changes by a certain amount, the other quantity always changes by a certain amount (for each day, there are 3 pennies added to the jar).
- Tables are a representation that can be used to show how one variable changes in relation to another.
- The same ratio relationship can occur in different contexts (e.g., 3 pennies per day, 3 cubes per "floor").

Patterns, Functions, and Change in Grades 3–5

In Grades 3–5, students focus on both linear and nonlinear change. Students study situations with a constant rate of change, in which two variables are related in ways that can be expressed in a verbal rule or an equation (such as the relationship between the total number of pennies in a jar and the number of days pennies have been collected, when a fixed number of pennies is added to the jar each day). They learn to take into account any starting amount (i.e., the number of pennies in the jar at the beginning) and the rate of change (i.e., the number of pennies added to the jar each day). They also study relationships in which the value of one variable cannot be determined based on the value of the other (such as the relationship between temperature and time in Grade 3 and between plant growth and time in Grade 4). In Grades 4 and 5, they also encounter situations in which the relationship between the two variables can be determined, but the change is not occurring at a constant rate, for example, a Penny Jar in which the number of pennies doubles each day.

Students work extensively with ways of representing relationships between two variables: with words, with tables and graphs, with numbers, and (starting in Grade 4) with symbolic notation. These units reinforce and connect with work in other units on multiplication, ratio, area, volume, and graphing. The Algebra Connections essay in each of the patterns, functions, and change units provides more detailed information about this sequence of students' work and how it connects to algebra.

Examples of ideas investigated in these units in Grades 3–5 (in addition to some of those in the K–2 list that continue to be studied in new contexts) are as follows:

- Line graphs are a representation that can show the relationship between two variables. A line graph represents both individual values of the variable and the rate of change of one variable in relation to another.
- In a situation with a constant rate of change, the value of one variable can be determined, given the value of the other.
- The relationship between two variables in a situation with a constant rate of change can be described in words and with symbolic notation.
- In some situations, the rate of change is determined but not constant. In these situations, the rate of change may be, for example, increasing by a constant amount.

Early Algebra Is Fundamental

Underlying the work in early algebra are, according to one of the *Investigations'* mathematician advisors, "foundational principles"—principles that connect elementary students' work in arithmetic to later work in algebra. For example, when second graders consider how changing the order of numbers in an addition or subtraction problem affects the sum or difference, they can engage in reasoning about foundational ideas, in this case, that addition is commutative, but subtraction is not: $a + b = b + a$, but $c - d \neq d - c$. Even though they may not yet have the experience with negative numbers to allow them to completely make sense of $14 - 26$, they see, through modeling and representing this problem, that it does not have the same difference as $26 - 14$. In later years, they will come to see that there *is* a regularity here, that if $c - d = a$, then $d - c = -a$, or $c - d = -(d - c)$.

Similarly, when fifth graders develop representations to show why halving one factor in a multiplication problem and doubling the other results in the same product, they are applying knowledge of foundational properties of multiplication and division. In later years, they may explain the more general claim that dividing one factor by any number (except 0) and multiplying the other factor by the same number maintains the same product by reference to the associative property of multiplication and to multiplication by 1—the identity element for multiplication. Through a series of steps, based on these properties of multiplication, one can show that, if a, b, and n are numbers $(n \neq 0)$, then $a \times b = a \times b \times \frac{n}{n} = (a \times n) \times \left(\frac{b}{n}\right)$.

For most adults, notation such as the use of variables, operations, and equal signs is the chief identifying feature of algebra. Although students use symbolic notation in Grades 4 and 5, the notation is not the focus of activity in Grades K–5. Underlying the notation are ways of reasoning about how the operations work. This *reasoning* about how numbers can be put together and taken apart under different operations or about relationships between two changing quantities, *not* the notation, is the central work of elementary students in algebra.

Algebra for All Students

Work in early algebra in the elementary classroom has the potential of enhancing the learning of *all* students. The teachers with whom the *Investigations* team collaborated during the development of the curriculum commented on this potential in their classrooms. Teacher collaborators reported that students who tend to have difficulty in mathematics become stronger mathematical thinkers through this work. As one teacher wrote, "When I began to work on generalizations with my students, I noticed a shift in my less capable learners. Things seemed more accessible to them." When the generalizations are made explicit—through language and representations used to justify them—they become accessible to more students and can become the foundation for greater computational fluency. Furthermore, the disposition to create a representation when a mathematical question arises supports students in reasoning through their confusions.

At the same time, students who generally outperform their peers in mathematics find this content challenging and stimulating. The study of numbers and operations extends beyond efficient computation to the excitement of making and proving conjectures about mathematical relationships that apply to an infinite class of numbers. A teacher explained, "Students develop a habit of mind of looking beyond the activity to search for something more, some broader mathematical context to fit the experience into."

Early algebra is not an add-on. The foundations of algebra arise naturally throughout students' work with numbers, operations, and patterns and by using familiar and accessible contexts to investigate how one set of values changes in relation to another. This work anchors students' concepts of the operations and underlies greater computational flexibility.

Teacher Note

Discussing Mathematical Ideas

Throughout the *Investigations* curriculum, whole-class discussion is a key aspect of students' mathematical activity. Class discussion provides a time for students to

- articulate their mathematical ideas.
- share different approaches to solving a problem.
- identify and investigate what they don't understand.
- analyze why a solution works or how it is flawed.
- pose conjectures and identify evidence to support them.
- collaborate to build ideas or solve problems.
- develop mathematical language.
- use representations to describe mathematical relationships.
- compare and connect students' various ideas, representations, and solutions.
- learn to consider and question each other's ideas.

By carefully selecting problems, representations, and solutions for the whole class to consider, the teacher focuses discussion on key mathematical ideas and works with the class as a whole to move students' thinking forward.

Building a Mathematical Community

In the first weeks of school, teachers help the class develop norms for classroom discussion and work with students on attitudes and behavior that will support productive math discussions. Most teachers find that they need to work quite explicitly with students throughout the school year to first establish and then maintain expectations for class discussion. During discussions, teachers keep the flow of ideas organized and remind students about the appropriate focus. For example, "Right now I want comments that are either agreeing with, disagreeing with, or commenting on Yolanda's idea," or, "So we now have three different approaches to this problem on the board. Is there a way in which Jill's is similar to Corey's?" Teachers also find opportunities to comment directly on student actions, behavior, and contributions that support productive discourse:

> Because Stephen was willing to talk through what was confusing him when he got an answer that he knew wasn't right, it seemed to really help all of us understand this kind of problem better.
>
> When Kamala put up her picture of the problem, I heard some of you say, "Ooh!" What was it you understood when you saw that picture? Did anyone else have a picture or a diagram that helped you understand how to solve this problem?

And from time to time teachers discuss directly with the class what aspects of class discussions have been helping or hindering students' participation:

> What helps you be willing to share your work or make an observation during class discussion? Are there times you don't feel comfortable speaking? Why is that?

Building an inclusive mathematics classroom involves a focus on respect for student ideas and acceptance of differences. Working on establishing this community with students will vary across grades and even from one year to another, depending on the needs and experiences of your students. (See the section "Setting Up the Mathematical Community" in Part 7, Working with the Range of Learners: Classroom Cases for some teachers' thoughts on building the classroom mathematics community.)

Focusing Class Discussions

Students' ideas are important and are, in fact, central to discussion. But if a discussion bounces among too many different ideas or tries to include too many different approaches, the discussion becomes ungrounded and hard for students to follow. Simply listing one problem-solving approach after another doesn't engage students beyond the few moments when they are contributing their own idea.

The Math Focus Points for Discussion and sample teacher dialogue found in the text for every discussion will help you guide the discussion. In preparing for class, ask yourself:

- What do I want this discussion to accomplish?
- What do I want all students to take away from this discussion?
- How will the time spent as a whole class enhance the work students have done individually or in pairs or groups?

During work that precedes the discussion, observe students' work with the upcoming discussion in mind. Ask yourself:

- What is a difficulty that many students are having?
- What is a problem that many students are struggling with?
- Is there a question that one pair or group came up with that it would be fruitful for the whole class to discuss?
- What are the basic approaches to solving this problem that students are using?
- Which students or groups have ideas or approaches that should be shared?

Student Participation

Whole-class discussion time is precious class time; it should serve to consolidate or move ahead the math thinking of all students. Find ways during discussions to elicit responses from different students. Although all students may not participate in any one discussion, all of your students' voices should be heard over the course of several discussions. There are many ways to work with students to encourage them to participate. For example, listen carefully to students' ideas and look carefully at their work during activities. Help particular students prepare to share one of their ideas. At first, some students might be more comfortable if you put their solution, representation, or idea on the board or a transparency and present it to the class yourself; alternatively, the student might explain a certain part of the solution, while you add to the student's explanation.

Think of ways to invite all students' participation during each discussion by asking students to raise hands if they used the same approach or if they agree or disagree with a statement you or another student makes. Pose a question and have students discuss it for a few minutes in pairs before having the whole class consider it. Use wait time judiciously and think about ways that students can use quiet signals when they are ready to respond (e.g., thumbs up rather than hands waving); then students who are still thinking are not distracted.

Ideas are bound to come up that you cannot pursue during class discussions. Sometimes you cannot follow or decipher a student's idea at the moment or you are not sure about how it relates to what is being discussed. If you don't understand what a student is saying, you might ask another student to interpret or talk to the student later. Don't be afraid to let students know that you have to think about something and get back to them or follow up with them after the discussion. You can always bring an idea back to the class later if you decide it would be important for the class to think about it.

You can find other ways to follow up on a student's idea that is not central or accessible for the whole class: "I was thinking about your idea, and here's a problem I thought you could try it on." Some teachers have a "parking lot" poster for ideas that come up during class but they don't have time to pursue. These ideas may come up again later or can be referred to when they become relevant. The better you know the curriculum, the more you will know when they might come up.

Setting Up the Classroom for Discussion

It is critical that students are sitting in such a way that everyone is focused on the discussion and everyone can hear. If there are representations that students need to see during the discussions, they must be large enough and dark enough so that everyone can see them.

A variety of seating arrangements for class discussions can work, as long as there are clear expectations connected to them. In some classrooms, students gather on a rug for the class meeting and then return to their places or choose places for work time. In other classrooms, students often stay at their own desks for meetings. Some teachers vary the setting, with students staying at their desks when the meeting will be short and gathering together when a longer time is needed.

To facilitate a smooth transition to meeting on the rug, some teachers assign students places to sit on the rug, changing them every month or so. Others place circles, mats, or white boards to clearly mark the places available for students to sit. Others allow students to sit wherever they want in a circle as long as they can see the teacher and all of the other students. They might remind students to make a good choice about sitting in a position and next to classmates that enables them to focus on the discussion. While some students can pay attention while sitting on the floor, others do better in a chair.

Guidelines for Whole-Class Discussions

In summary, here are some guidelines to keep in mind for your class's whole-group discussions:

- Set up norms and review them frequently; point out examples in which they are working.
- Plan a clear purpose and focus for each discussion, based on the listed Focus Points.
- Use wait time to give students time to think.
- Ask students to use quiet student signals to indicate they are ready to respond.
- Prepare with some students ahead of time to participate in the discussion.
- Have clear visuals that everyone can see and refer to.
- Establish a routine arrangement that ensures that everyone can hear and see.
- Select only a few students to share solutions.

When all students come to a discussion prepared to listen actively and to contribute ideas, the class discussions provide an important forum in which they can articulate, represent, connect, and consolidate the mathematical ideas they have been working on.

Racial and Linguistic Diversity in the Classroom: What Does Equity Mean in Today's Math Classroom?

... we have no patterns for relating across our human differences as equals. As a result, those differences have been misnamed and misused in the service of separation and confusion.[1]

Audre Lorde

We must not, in trying to think about how we can make a big difference, ignore the small daily differences we can make, which, over time, add up to big differences that we often cannot foresee.[2]

Marian Wright Edelman

U.S. public schools are responsible for educating students who are more racially and linguistically diverse than at any other time in our history. The beginning of the 21st century in the United States is marked by an influx of immigrants, and schools and teachers are at the front door meeting these students. Hence, many teachers work in classrooms with increasing numbers of immigrant students, students of color, and linguistically diverse students who often face unique challenges related to language proficiency, cultural and social adaptation, and poverty. What are the issues and challenges for teachers in these diverse classrooms?

While developing this curriculum, the *Investigations* staff and field-test teachers worked together to continue educating ourselves about this question. Many of us have had direct experience teaching in schools where students come from diverse racial, cultural, and linguistic backgrounds. In many cases, the students' culture, race, ethnicity, and first language are different from those of the teacher. This Teacher Note provides a glimpse into the complex issues about racial, cultural, and linguistic diversity being discussed in the field of education today. It also provides resources for further reading, including those we found helpful in our own professional development.

[1]From a paper delivered at the Copeland Colloquium, Amherst College, in April, 1980. The paper was entitled, "Age, Race, Class, and Sex: Women Redefining Difference."

[2]Marian Wright Edelman, "Families in Peril: An Agenda for Social Change," The W. E. B. Du Bois Lectures (Cambridge, Mass.: Harvard University Press, 1987), p. 107.

Equity in the Mathematics Classroom

> Equity does not mean that every student should receive identical instruction; instead, it demands that reasonable and appropriate accommodations be made as needed to promote access and attainment for all students. (NCTM, 2000, p. 11)

Investigations was developed with the assumption that all learners can engage in challenging and substantive mathematics. Assumptions about students' capacity and inclination to learn in school can undermine their access to and participation in significant mathematics learning. An extensive body of literature documents the persistence of these assumptions and their effects on students' opportunity to learn. For example, students of color and those whose first language is not English are often seen in terms of what they lack instead of what they bring to the learning environment (termed in the literature a *deficit thinking* model). Student underperformance in school may be explained by student and family shortcomings, behavior that does not match a particular set of norms, immaturity, or lack of intelligence. Students who do not speak fluent English may be judged as having poor or underdeveloped conceptual understanding because they cannot yet express the complexity of their thinking in English. Misunderstanding cultural differences can lead schools to inappropriately place children into special education and low-ability groups and to expect less from them than from other children. For instance, Entwistle and Alexander (1989) report that poor black children are often described as less mature, and, consequently, school personnel may hold lower expectations for them than for children whose socioeconomic status is higher.

Many teachers are working hard to improve learning opportunities for these students, with the goal of enhancing both the learning climate and students' educational performance. In this work, teachers must consider the broader issues as well as practices, procedures, strategies, and other key aspects of schooling. In an educational setting, equity indicates a state in which all children—students of color and white students, males and females, successful students and those who have fallen behind, and students who have been denied access in the past—have equal opportunities to learn, participate in challenging programs, and have equal access to the services they need to benefit from that education. Equity has sometimes been oversimplified to mean that all students should be treated the same—neutrally and without differentiation. Rather, differences matter, and matter in specific ways. Successful learning experiences depend on teachers building on the contributions of all students and recognizing the differences that matter to them.

In the mathematics education literature, researchers from four projects, three in the United States and one in South Africa, looked across their projects to identify features of classrooms "essential for supporting students' understanding" in mathematics (Hiebert et al., 1997). They organize these in five dimensions, one of which is "equity and accessibility." The authors describe this dimension as fundamental:

> [E]quity . . . is not an add-on or an optional dimension. It is an integral part of a system of instruction that sets students' understanding of mathematics as the goal. Without equity, the other dimensions are restricted and the system does not function well. (p. 12)

Race and Linguistic Diversity

While teaching a seminar on race in education several years ago, one of the authors of this essay was met with a remarkable silence and little open discussion of race, racism, and the ways they come up in classroom teaching. Some think that racism is no longer an issue in schools, and that "color blindness" is the way to approach a diverse class of students. However, many in the field believe that explicit classroom attention to race, ethnicity, and home language results in increased communication and learning.

Race (or ethnicity) can have overlapping and coexisting categories of meaning. Sometimes, race signifies being economically, socially, politically, and educationally oppressed. Other times it signifies a sense of community and belonging, involving valuable associations with a particular group, history, cultural codes, and sensibilities. Race conveys multiple meanings, and racism takes on multiple forms, subject to context and situation. Whether expressed subtly or with crude directness, the effects of racism are felt in everyday school experience. Preconceptions about who students are, which are based on surface behaviors, can mask important potential.

For example, in one classroom, a Hmong girl is quiet, well behaved, and does little to demand attention. But although she is well behaved, she is not engaged and does not quite know what's going on in the lesson. In another classroom, a young black boy is distracted and disruptive, eager to contribute, but often "in trouble." The Hmong girl might be seen as a model student—quiet, hard working, high achieving, and nonchallenging of classroom norms. In contrast, the black boy might be seen as loud, threatening, noncompliant, dysfunctional, and low achieving. The characterization of the Hmong girl seems positive, even flattering, in comparison to the characterization of the black boy. However, both views may be silencing the voices, needs, and potential contributions of these children in different ways. For the Hmong girl, a focus on seemingly compliant behavior may lead the teacher to ignore her educational needs. For the black boy, a focus on seemingly bad behavior may distract the teacher from recognizing his educational strengths.

To understand all students' experiences—to support them in rigorous learning and to respect the variety of their language practices, histories, and identities—educators must continue to learn about the issues of race and racism, cultural and linguistic diversity, and teaching practices and strategies that support the learning of all students.

Teaching Practices and Strategies

Many important insights about teaching practices and strategies that support students of color and English language learners can be gleaned from those who have been studying and writing in the field. Some of these educators and researchers focus specifically on the mathematics classroom, but there are also accounts from science and literacy that have a great deal to offer the teaching of mathematics.

Gloria Ladson-Billings studied exemplary teachers of African-American students and has written about an approach of "culturally relevant teaching." Although the teachers she studied differed in the way they structured their classrooms—some appeared more "traditional," while others were more "progressive" in their teaching strategies—their conceptions of and beliefs about teaching and learning had many commonalities. Here is a subset of characteristics of these teachers adapted from Ladson-Billings' list (1995). These teachers:

- believed that all students are capable of academic success.
- saw their pedagogy as always in process.
- developed a community of learners.
- encouraged students to learn collaboratively and be responsible for each other.
- believed that knowledge is shared, recycled, and constructed.
- believed they themselves must be passionate about learning.
- believed they must scaffold, or build bridges, to facilitate learning.
- believed assessment must be multifaceted.

Overall, these teachers supported their students and held them to high standards:

> Students were not permitted to choose failure in their classrooms. They cajoled, nagged, pestered, and bribed the students to work at high intellectual levels. Absent from their discourse was the "language of lacking." . . . Instead, teachers talked about their own shortcomings and limitations and ways they needed to change to ensure student success. (p. 479)

Critical to teaching students who bring a variety of cultural, social, and linguistic experience into the classroom is what Marilyn Cochran-Smith (1995b) calls "understanding children's understanding":

> [C]entral to learning to teach in a culturally and linguistically diverse society is understanding children's understanding or exploring what it means to know a child, to consider his or her background, behaviors, and interactions with others, and to try to do what Duckworth calls "give reason" to the ways the child constructs meanings and interpretations, drawing on experiences and knowledge developed both inside and outside the classroom. (p. 511)

Eleanor Duckworth, whom Cochran-Smith cites above, may have originated the phrase *understanding children's understanding* in her essay of the same name (1996). In that essay, she discusses the idea of "giving children reason" as she describes a group of teachers in a study group who set themselves this challenge: "[E]very time a child did or said something whose meaning was not immediately obvious . . . [they] sought to understand the way in which . . . [it] could be construed to make sense" (pp. 86–87).

This work of hearing and understanding students' ideas, discourse, and representations and involving all of them in significant intellectual work can be especially challenging when students come from backgrounds quite different from the teacher's own. Cindy Ballenger's *Teaching Other People's Children* (1999) and Vivian Paley's *White Teacher* (1989) provide first-person accounts of teachers who are actively examining their own preconceptions about the behavior and discourse of the students they teach. Ballenger expresses how her initial belief that all students could learn was not enough:

> I began with these children expecting deficits, not because I believed they or their background was deficient—I was definitely against such a view—but because I did not know how to see their strengths . . . I came to see . . . strengths . . . that are part of an intellectual tradition, not always a schooled tradition, but an intellectual one nonetheless, and one that, therefore, had a great deal to say to teaching and learning. (p. 3)

Ballenger recounts her journey in learning to listen to the sense of her students, both "honoring the child's home discourse" and engaging the student in "school-based and discipline-based ways of talking, acting, and knowing" (p. 6).

Working in English with students whose first language is not English presents two challenges to teachers who do not share the student's first language: (1) how to learn about, respect, and support the discourse practices that students can contribute from their own knowledge and communities; and (2) how to bring students into the language of the discipline of mathematics in English. Judit Moschkovich (1999) identifies two critical functions of mathematical discussions for English language learners: "uncovering the mathematical content in student contributions and bringing different ways of talking and points of view into contact" (p. 11). She identifies several important instructional strategies that support these students' participation in math discussions (p. 11):

- using several expressions for the same concept
- using gestures and objects to clarify meaning
- accepting and building on student responses
- revoicing student statements with more technical terms
- focusing not only on vocabulary development but also on mathematical content and argumentation practices

Josiane Hudicourt-Barnes (2003) writes about the participation of students whose home language is Haitian Creole. Her research highlights the way that understanding the forms of discourse students contribute from their own culture enables teachers to uncover and appreciate how students are making sense of subject matter. Although she writes about science learning, her observations are applicable to the mathematics classroom: "To be 'responsive to the children and responsible to the subject matter' (Ball, 1997, p. 776), we must be able to hear children's diverse voices and create opportunities for them to pursue their ideas and questions (p. 17)." Further, she argues that classroom discourse that follows a rigid, restrictive format "may mean that children from families of non-Western traditions are shut out of classroom participation and that skills from other traditions are devalued and subtracted from children's cognitive repertoires, and therefore also made unavailable to their fellow students" (p. 17).

Being "responsive to the children and responsive to the subject matter" is highlighted by many of the writers in this field. They emphasize that the teacher's responsibility is *both* to the students' ideas, sense making, and forms of discourse *and* to bringing these students in to the ideas, vocabulary, and ways of working in the discipline of the content area. Gloria Ladson-Billings (2002) sums up her observations of a teacher whose urban, largely African American, students, initially hated writing:

> To meet the academic goals he had set, Carter had to rethink his practice in some fundamental ways. . . . He had to keep a sense of uncertainty and a willingness to question in the forefront of his teaching. . . . while Carter empathized with the students' struggle to write he understood that his job was to teach them to do it. He didn't put them down for not enjoying writing or writing well, but he also did not let them off the hook. He had to help them appreciate the power and fulfillment of writing and he had to preserve each student's sense of self. (p. 118)

Continuing to Learn

Continuing to learn is something we all can do. This Teacher Note attempts only to introduce you to some authors and resources who can contribute to that learning. Many of the resources cited here include rich examples from classrooms that can evoke productive interaction when read and discussed with peers. You may have opportunities to take advantage of courses, seminars, or study groups, such as the one that Lawrence and Tatum (1997) describe, or to self-organize peer discussions of articles in the field.

Teachers can also pose their own questions and study their own classrooms. Writing brief case studies in which you raise your own questions about these issues in your teaching and then sharing your writing can be a rich source of learning. You might start by reading what other teachers have written about their own practice as they reflect on their teaching of diverse students. For example, in *What's Happening in Math Class?* (Schifter, 1996), Alissa Sheinbach writes about three students who are struggling in mathematics (vol. 1, pp. 115–129), Allen Gagnon writes about his Spanish-speaking students (vol. 1, pp. 129–136), and Nora Toney recounts her own experiences with racism as a student (when she was bused into a largely white school) and later as a teacher herself (vol. 2, pp. 26–36). After describing some successful experiences in mathematics she had as an adult that contrasted with her experience in the "low group" as a student, Toney concludes by identifying factors that have been important to her own learning:

> I have discovered the ingredients necessary for me to learn and achieve success: high teacher expectation, fairness, inclusiveness, engaging contextual material, constant monitoring and feedback, discussions/debates, and reflective writing. Generally speaking, I need numerous opportunities to connect my thinking and ideas to new concepts and ideas. These factors facilitated my *learning* of mathematics, so now I am trying to incorporate these same factors into *teaching* mathematics. (p. 36)

References and Additional Readings

Ball, D. (1997). What do students know? Facing challenges of distance, context, and desire in trying to hear children. In T. Biddle, T. Good, & I. Goodson (Eds.), *International handbook on teachers and teaching* (pp. 769–817). Dordrecht, Netherlands: Kluwer Press.

Ballenger, C. (1999). *Teaching other people's children: Literacy and learning in a bilingual classroom.* New York: Teachers College Press.

Cochran-Smith, M. (1995a). Uncertain allies: Understanding the boundaries of race and teaching. *Harvard Educational Review,* 63, 541–570.

Cochran-Smith, M. (1995b). Color blindness and basket making are not the answers: Confronting the dilemmas of race, culture, and language diversity in teacher education. *American Educational Research Journal,* 32, 493–522.

Duckworth, E. (1996). *"The having of wonderful ideas" and other essays on teaching and learning.* New York: Teachers College Press.

Entwistle, D., and Alexander, K. (1989). Early schooling as a "critical period" phenomenon. In K. Namboodiri & R. Corwin (Eds.), *Research in Sociology of Education and Socialization,* Volume 8, (pp. 27–55) Greenwich, CT: Jai Press.

Heath, S. B. (1983). *Ways with words: Language, life, and work in communities and classrooms.* New York: Cambridge University Press.

Hiebert, J., Carpenter, T. P., Fennema, E., Fuson, K. C., Wearne, D., Murray, H., et al. (1997). *Making sense: Teaching and learning mathematics with understanding.* Portsmouth, NH: Heinemann.

Hudicourt-Barnes, J. (2003). The use of argumentation in Haitian Creole science classrooms. *Harvard Educational Review,* 73(1), 73–93.

King, J. (1991). Dysconscious racism: Ideology, identity, and the miseducation of teachers. *The Journal of Negro Education,* 60, 133–146.

Ladson-Billings, G. (1994). *The dreamkeepers: Successful teaching for African American students.* San Francisco: Jossey-Bass.

Ladson-Billings, G. (1995). Toward a theory of culturally relevant pedagogy. *American Educational Research Journal,* 32, 465–491.

Ladson-Billings, G. (2002). I ain't writin' nuttin': Permission to fail and demands to succeed in urban classrooms. In L. Delpit & J. K. Dowdy (Eds.), *The skin that we speak: Thoughts on language and culture in the classroom* (pp. 107–120). New York: The New Press.

Lawrence, S. M., & Tatum, B. D. (1997). White educators as allies: Moving from awareness to action. In M. Fine, L. Weis, L. C. Powell, & L. M. Wong (Eds.), *Off white: Readings on race, power, and society* (pp. 333–342). New York: Routledge.

Lewis, A. (2003). *Race in the schoolyard: Negotiating the color line in classrooms and communities.* New Brunswick, New Jersey and London: Rutgers University Press.

Moschkovich, J. (1999). Supporting the participation of English language learners in mathematical discussions. *For the Learning of Mathematics,* 19(1), 11–19.

National Council of Teachers of Mathematics. (2000). *Principles and standards for school mathematics.* Reston, VA: Author.

Obidah, J., & Teel, K. M. (1996). The impact of race on cultural differences on the teacher/student relationship: A collaborative classroom study by an African American and Caucasian teacher research team. *Kansas Association for Supervision and Curriculum Development Record,* 14, 70–86.

Obidah, J., & Teel, K. M. (2001). *Because of the kids.* New York: Teachers College Press.

Paley, V. G. (1989). *White teacher.* Cambridge, MA: Harvard University Press.

Schifter, D. (1996). *What's happening in math class? Vol. 1: Envisioning new practices through teacher narratives ; Vol. 2: Reconstructing professional identities.* New York: Teachers College Press.

Titles of Grade 4 Teacher Notes by Unit

Unit 6 Fraction Cards and Decimal Squares

Unit 7 Moving Between Solids and Silhouettes

Unit 8 How Many Packages? How Many Groups?

Unit 9 Penny Jars and Plant Growth

PART 7

Working with the Range of Learners

Preview

All teachers are faced with the challenge of meeting the needs of a range of learners in their classrooms. The range of learners can include students who struggle in certain areas of mathematics, those who excel in math, students who are English Language Learners, and students who have particular learning needs.

This section contains a series of case studies written by fourth-grade teachers from urban, suburban, and rural schools, telling how they implemented the *Investigations* program in their classrooms. The students in these classrooms vary on many dimensions, including gender, language, culture and ethnicity, and special needs. They present a range of strengths and needs in their prior experience with mathematics and their confidence in the classroom.

Through their writing, these teachers bring us into their classrooms and invite us to participate in how they think about supporting their range of learners. As they captured moments in time in their classrooms, the teachers did not intend to provide exemplary actions to be emulated or a how-to manual of what to do for particular students or with particular activities. Rather, they offer the kind of thinking teachers do as a matter of course in their teaching. Through the hundreds of interactions they have with their students each day, teachers try to understand what those students bring to their learning and how to support them in moving further. In these case studies, they share some of that thinking.

We collected these cases together in this book, rather than including them with the curriculum units, because they are not designed to illustrate "how to do" a particular activity. Rather, as a group, they provide examples and questions to inspire your own questioning and reflection. You may want to use this set of cases on your own or discuss them with a group of colleagues.

Keep in mind that each case provides only a glimpse into a teacher's classroom. Just as you would not expect anyone to understand the complexity of the issues you face in your own classroom from such a brief glimpse, the cases cannot provide all the background information you might need to understand a particular teacher's decision with a particular student on a particular day. But you do not need to know more detail to use these cases for your own professional development. Use them as starting points when considering similar issues that you face with your students. The questions at the end of each case provide a starting point for discussion. If you discuss these cases with colleagues in a cross-grade group, you will have even more examples to consider by combining the sets of cases from two or more grades.

The classroom cases are grouped into three themes, focusing on some of the most important issues teachers face as they work to meet the needs of their students. In the first section, "Setting Up the Mathematical Community," teachers write about how they create a supportive and productive learning environment in their classrooms. In the second section, "Accommodations for Learning," teachers focus on specific modifications they make to meet the needs of some of their learners. Because these teachers chose to write about particular students in their classrooms, the cases do not cover all the kinds of needs and accommodations you might encounter. However, even though the specific students discussed may differ from students in your own classroom, these teachers consistently found that accommodations they had made for one student often spilled over to benefit other students with related needs. In the last section, "Language and Representation," teachers share how they help students use representations and develop language to investigate and express mathematical ideas.

There is, of course, much overlap. Some cases illustrate ideas that could fall into more than one of these sections. You will find ideas from one section cropping up in the cases in other sections. For example, when teachers develop accommodations for learning, they are often using mathematical representations or helping students connect their language to the mathematical ideas.

Note: Pseudonyms have been used for all student and teacher names.

Summary of Cases

Setting Up the Mathematical Community

Who Are the Students in My Classroom? What Do They Think?

Nadia Cortes facilitates a discussion that enables her class to create norms that begin to shape the mathematical community.

Incorrect Answers as Learning Opportunities

A discussion about what can be learned from wrong answers helps Melanie Lloyd's class create a safe environment for sharing mathematical ideas.

Student Grouping That Enhances Learning

Kellie Sullivan shares the purposeful way she groups her students for a Math Workshop.

Accommodations for Learning

The Case of Norma: Understanding the Relationship Between Feet and Yards

Nadia Cortes helps Norma connect what she understands about multiplication and division to her work with measurement.

Accommodations in an Inclusion Classroom: Silhouettes of Cube Buildings

John Ryder prepares for a lesson by anticipating the challenges his students may face and thinking about how he can support their learning.

Providing Modifications and Checking Assumptions: How Many 4s Are in 1,500?

Molly Levy challenges some of her more capable math students and finds that some of the knowledge they have about numbers breaks down when they move to larger numbers.

The Case of Maura: Now That I Know the Exact Answer I Can Figure Out the Estimate: Helping a Student Understand Estimation

Melanie Lloyd finds out what Maura does and does not understand about estimation and helps her move toward better estimation strategies.

The Case of Kevin and Dejara: Multiplying by Multiples of 10

Sarah Peck teaches a lesson that helps two of her students develop building blocks for multidigit multiplication.

Language and Representation

Creating a Supportive Environment for Hedson

Melanie Lloyd shares how she created a supportive environment for an English Language Learner, enabling him to share his ideas with the rest of the class.

Helping Students Make Sense of Penny Jar Problems: Using an Array Representation

Norma Bell creates a visual representation to help her students use more efficient strategies for solving Penny Jar problems.

Setting Up the Mathematical Community

Who Are the Students in My Classroom? What Do They Think?

Nadia Cortes is a fourth-grade teacher. To create a successful math community for her students, she starts at the beginning of the school year to build a safe environment in which students can take risks and share their thoughts and ideas. Taking the first steps toward this goal, she plans a math discussion in which she asks students to describe the ideal or perfect math class. Her hope is that through this discussion her students will brainstorm a set of guidelines that will form the foundation for how they will operate in math class. When the discussion takes an unanticipated turn, she is surprised about what she learns from her students.

I asked my students to describe their ideal math class. To be able to work on class norms, I needed to know what their expectations and experiences were. It surprised me to find out how vulnerable they felt. It also astonished me that I was surprised by their vulnerability.

Mara started the discussion by sharing that having a perfect teacher would make a perfect math class. I asked her to describe what she meant, and the following conversation ensued.

Mara: If I don't understand something, she [the teacher] would explain things without getting mad.

Gilly: Yes, I hate it when I don't understand something. I said it to this girl last year, and she made this face [Gilly makes a face that looks incredulous], like how can you not get it? [Many kids laugh and agree with Gilly.]

Norma: And I hate it when the teacher says, "I should see all hands going up" because if your hand does not go up you feel stupid that you didn't get it.

Before I knew it, the focus had changed to "what problems do you find in a math class that is *not* going well?" My students became very excited during the conversation and needed to talk at length about their feelings. After awhile, I refocused them on how to address some of their issues rather than just complain. I wanted them to find solutions we could all follow in the class that would help us build a productive math community.

I was dismayed at how fragile my students felt about math. I realized that I too had my mind on an "ideal class." In this ideal class students would come feeling strong and secure in their math ideas and would confidently tackle their errors. Strong kids, confident kids, secure kids. Instead, what I was looking at was fragility, delicacy, insecurity, and the fear of making mistakes—hiding mistakes from others for fear of being called silly or dumb. What experiences had cracked their confidence and opened wounds they needed to protect?

At this point, Ms. Cortes decides to talk with her students about her own feelings of insecurity when she works on mathematics with groups of adults. She lets them know that she is a learner as well, with similar feelings of fragility. Romina then initiates the following conversation:

Romina: Yes, I hate it when I don't get it, and it is not easy for me to say it.

Teacher: What can we do to allow you to say something? What would work for you?

Gilly: I would like to get help from anybody. So if I don't get it in class, then anybody, teacher or kid, can help me.

Teacher: What you're saying is that a class in which we all help each other, without making each other feel dumb, would help you learn better?

Gilly: Exactly! [Many students are nodding their heads in agreement.]

Norma: I hate it when kids say, "That's easy."

Teacher: What would work for you?

Norma: If they say it, we can say, "Can you explain it to me please?" If they know, they can explain it. If they don't, they are showing off and maybe they won't say it again. [The students laugh.]

As my students headed to their physical education class, I think they were relieved to take a break from thinking about how incompetent they can sometimes feel. But they were also excited because they were able to talk about these feelings openly. I think that this was an important conversation we had to have because we have all felt this way before. I hope they continue talking about these issues as they come up.

By giving students an opportunity to share their thoughts about what creates a perfect math class, Ms. Cortes allows them to participate in the development of classroom norms to guide how they will successfully work together. As she listens carefully to what the students are saying, she gains a lot of insight about her learners. Her keen attention to their comments allows her to go beneath the surface of their suggestions to understand why they are making them. This discussion not only gives the students an opportunity to develop norms; they also learn that they are in a place where their thoughts matter and they will be heard. As they move forward in their math work, and get to know each other better as individual learners with different needs, their community norms will have to be revisited and revised.

Questions for Discussion

1. **What strategies might Ms. Cortes model for the whole class to help students feel safe to express confusions?**
2. **How can Ms. Cortes create structures to encourage students to help each other in respectful ways?**
3. **Have there been times when you have shared your own mathematics experiences with your students? What was your goal, and how did your students react?**

Incorrect Answers as Learning Opportunities

As Melanie Lloyd begins the school year, she thinks about how to establish the critical thinking skills that support productive discussions about mathematical ideas. Her first step toward creating this type of math community is ensuring that all learners feel safe and encouraging students to participate in mathematical discussions. To this end, Ms. Lloyd starts early in the year to help her students learn the importance of studying incorrect answers as part of mathematical discussions.

Early work to establish a respectful culture of learning is especially crucial for math class. It is during math time that competition interferes with listening to and working with each other. Students tend to devalue the process of working through a problem as they clamor to deliver the right answer. The constant challenge for teachers is to support both the faster and slower problem solvers and to model patience and listening by all students.

During the first few days of math class, I often focus on wrong answers to help establish a respectful, attentive, and inclusive math culture. Almost every day we start math class with a question the students solve in their math journals. The students show how they solved the problem, and we discuss the problem and share our strategies. One math journal assignment that I presented was as follows:

How many different expressions can you make that equal 25?

I informed the students that they could use addition, subtraction, multiplication, division, or any combination of those operations.

In all classrooms, students must at times grapple with their own incorrect responses as well as with those of their peers. Ms. Lloyd knows that by simply asking students to share, incorrect answers are likely to surface. How incorrect responses are managed is critical in developing a sense of safety and risk-taking when students share ideas and strategies. Ms. Lloyd seeks to convey to her students what it means to question and analyze responses in a productive manner. When Andrew offers an answer that is incorrect, Ms. Lloyd uses this opportunity to model possible responses.

Andrew: I have a way to get to 25: $6 \times 4 + 2$.

Teacher: I'll write this one down with the others so we can check it out.

Nadine: I don't know if that equals 25.

I notice that Andrew begins to frown and squirm.

Teacher: So, you have a different answer from Andrew. Andrew, do you want to look at your number sentence again?

Like many students, Andrew is flustered by this approach. He is silent, not sure if he's correct and unsure of what to do next.

Teacher: Let's talk through this together. Is that okay? [Andrew nods.]

Teacher: Where should we start? You say to start at the answer to 6×4. What is 6×4?

Andrew: I think it's 24. Wait, yes. It says so on the times table chart.

Teacher: Then what?

Andrew: I added 2 to 24 to get . . . wait, that equals 26.

Teacher: Can you remember what you were thinking when you first did this sentence?

Andrew: I think I started counting in the wrong place. I think I counted 24, instead of from 24.

Teacher: Who else sometimes counts from the wrong number? [A few hands are raised.]

Kiyanna: Sometimes I get lost, and I have to start the problem all over again.

Sam: I do that, too. Sometimes I write the number on my paper to help keep track.

Teacher: It sounds as if some of you have found a technique for remembering. Thank you, Andrew, for sharing this example with us. It brought up some important points about solving math problems and how we can all learn from discussing our mistakes.

In this short exchange, we see students beginning to discuss their own experiences with incorrect answers or procedures. Ms. Lloyd is careful not to make Andrew the target of the conversation; she uses the example he provides to engage the entire class in a discussion that will help lay the foundation for future mathematical conversations. It is Ms. Lloyd's goal that students become comfortable analyzing incorrect answers so that they are more willing to offer their own solutions as part of the class process. With consistent reinforcement of this idea by the teacher and students alike, all learners can become comfortable participating in discussions, and the class will have the benefit of analyzing many different mathematical strategies.

Questions for Discussion

1. **In what ways does Ms. Lloyd turn Andrew's error into a "teachable moment"?**

2. **How do you build a safe environment in your classroom in which incorrect responses can be used as opportunities for learning and reflection by all students?**

Student Grouping That Enhances Learning

Student grouping for mathematics instruction is an area that has received widespread attention in recent years. Some educators believe that homogeneous (ability) grouping is a way to ensure that students obtain specific experiences and skills needed to move their thinking forward. Others feel that heterogeneous grouping offers students a chance to share their thinking across ability levels, leading to increased understanding of concepts and topics for all students. In either case, educators must consider the intersection of mathematical content, student ability, and experiences when grouping students for mathematics instruction. They think flexibly about student grouping, according to the demands of the task.

Kellie Sullivan, a fourth-grade teacher, describes her thinking about student grouping for a Math Workshop on multiplication. She bases her decisions on her students' unique mathematical and social contributions, personalities, and dispositions.

As I considered my students and thought about where they were in developing strategies for multiplication, I decided to partner them deliberately and have the partners remain together for the entire Math Workshop. Although I sometimes hear teachers talk about this sort of partnering as a form of ability grouping, I was thinking more of partnerships that would stimulate thinking and forward movement for each and every student. I thought about where students' thinking was at the moment, what sort of nudge I felt they needed to move forward, and which classmates might provide that opportunity.

As I introduced the activities to my students, I was quite explicit about the reasons for the partners. I said:

This Math Workshop will last several days, and I have chosen a partner for you whom I think will help you learn in a certain way. Your partner may be someone who is thinking in the same way you are, so you can solve the problems together and help each other. Or your partner may be someone who thinks a bit differently and can show you a new and interesting way to solve the problems. Either way, your partner will help you learn.

For example, one of the partnerships that I formed was between Dan and Kalina, partly because they get along well together. While Kalina can be challenging for others to work with, her math skills are strong, and she is confident with multiplication cluster problems and thinking her way through them. Dan, on the other hand, often gets stuck and doesn't know how to start. He has the social skills to deal with Kalina's prickly personality, and she has the clarity of thinking to help Dan move forward mathematically.

I partnered Lesa and Nathan because Lesa was quite articulate and confident about strategies she had developed while working with our remedial math teacher, Ms. Richmond. Nathan needed to become more flexible in his strategies and more articulate about them. They were working on similar strategies, but I felt Lesa might help Nathan develop more flexibility, while she would benefit from the need to explain to him. Because they both liked to write, I expected they would enjoy developing their written explanations together. In addition, Lesa is able to stay on task during open-ended activities, and Nathan needs support to stay focused.

Chase and Jillian, both strong math thinkers, were partners. Chase has a difficult time explaining his thinking clearly and completely, while Jillian is comfortable sticking with writing her explanations until they are complete. I thought she would be challenged trying to understand his thinking, while he might progress in being able to explain his thinking.

Jamal and Tarana are two strong students whom I paired together. Both of them use the standard algorithm. Although they are usually successful in solving problems and both insisted they "like this way the best," I was convinced they were capable of thinking much more deeply and flexibly. I was concerned that they were not flexible in approaching problems and that they did not always look at the problem as a whole before trying to solve it. I also knew they could deepen their understanding of multiplication by trying some other methods. As I handed out their folders, I specifically addressed this issue privately with them:

I'm having you be partners because I want you to work together to figure out other good ways to solve these problems. I know you can both do them that way, but sometimes there are other efficient ways to solve this kind of problem. I want you to find them.

Interestingly, they both grinned and looked as if they meant to rise to the challenge.

Matt and Spencer both often have unconventional but mathematically sound ways to solve problems. They also both tend to make careless errors and arrive at incorrect answers. As they began to work, I addressed this issue with them:

I have put you together because you are both really good math thinkers, but you often get the wrong answer. I want you to check each other carefully. Make sure you understand each other's methods, and that you have the correct answer at the end.

As I watched all of the partners begin work, I was pleased with the energy and cooperation that was evident in the room. Each partnership had complementary skills that were helping them stay focused, get into the problems, and move along. Each evening I collected the folders and went through them, noting work completed and, especially, strategies used. Each new day, I gave specific instructions about my expectations to each set of partners. I made up a set of challenge problems for some groups of students whom I felt needed to extend their thinking.

However, I began to worry a bit about a couple of students, including Dan. Dan's written work did not indicate that he was able to solve the cluster problems independently, and I wondered if his partnership was really helping him as I had hoped. Dan had completed very little work, and, at one point, I observed his partner, Kalina, standing by Dan's desk and coaching him about what to write on his paper. This, combined with the fact that he did not include a written explanation with any of his work, made me wonder if he had just copied the answers from Kalina. The next day, I decided to regroup a few partners so I could work individually with Dan and some other students. As we sat at the back table, I was relieved to discover that Dan understood more than his written work indicated. He was solving the problem 6×50. When I asked him, "Can you tell me how you got these answers?" he easily responded with mathematically accurate and sensible explanations. I then said, "Write that down just the way you said it." Dan wrote:

I knew $3 \times 50 = 150$. Six is the doble [double] of 3 so I doubled the 150 to get 300.

As I reviewed the work of the remaining partners, I saw the growth I had been hoping for.

- Chase, with Jillian's support, had been able to write explanations for all of his problems, which he had been unable to do before.
- Lesa and Nathan, too, had finished all the pages and had time to play a game. Their work was complete, organized, and accurate.
- I smiled to note that Spencer and Matt had completed a good deal of work and, although I had asked them to correct a few things, for the most part their answers were clear and accurate.
- Although Tarana had been absent for part of the Math Workshop, she and Jamal had completed a good deal of work. Jamal, when given the chance to substitute challenge problems for the required work, moved ahead a good deal. He worked with sustained interest on the problems I had made up for him, figuring each one out before checking it with great pleasure on the calculator. He was demonstrating the flexibility that I had hoped he would develop in his strategies, even with very difficult problems.

As I thought back about the Math Workshop we had finished, I realized my own thinking about the purpose of the activities had evolved as well. I used to think Math Workshop was for practicing skills and strategies. This time, however, I had specifically identified places where each student needed to grow. I had chosen partners based on my assessment of all students. I thought about students who would inspire other students in their mathematical development, and I told students what I expected of their partnerships. Given those expectations and my own clarity about mathematical growth instead of just rote practice, I believe that my students accomplished more during those three days than might have otherwise been the case.

Cooperative grouping in mathematics can be an important strategy for enhancing learning, but all too often cooperative groups are formed without careful attention to the ways in which students might support each other's mathematical thinking. Grouping is sometimes done strictly according to mathematical ability or to create a mix of students in terms of gender, race and ethnicity, and language preferences. Sometimes groups are self-chosen so that many students consistently work with the same individuals.

Ms. Sullivan illustrates a more complex way of thinking about student groupings that takes into consideration students' mathematical abilities, as well as their personalities and her own mathematical goals for each student. Ms. Sullivan makes her expectations clear for students, reviews the purpose of the partnerships, provides regular check-ins, and alters pairings when they appear not to meet her expectations. Her approach provides students with numerous opportunities to work in a variety of thoughtfully chosen groupings.

Questions for Discussion

1. **What factors about her students did Ms. Sullivan take into account as she planned how to group them?**

2. **Why do you think she chose to make her decisions explicit to her students? Do you agree with this decision?**

3. **In what ways do you use flexible grouping to meet the needs of the students in your classroom? What factors do you take into account as you plan your groups?**

Accommodations for Learning

The Case of Norma: Understanding the Relationship Between Feet and Yards

It is December, and the students in Ms. Cortes's fourth-grade class have just finished mapping paths of 100 feet. Ms. Cortes realizes that although her student Norma was able to use a yardstick to measure the path, she was confused about the relationships among the measuring units. In this case, Ms. Cortes tries to figure out what Norma knows and how she can help Norma build on that knowledge.

Teacher: So, you used the yardstick and measured 100 feet. How many times did you use the yardstick to count?

Norma: 100.

Teacher: How many feet are in a yardstick?

Norma: 1.

Teacher: Do you remember when we used a ruler to measure, and we said it was a foot long?

Norma: Yes.

Teacher: Is the yardstick the same size as a ruler?

Norma: No.

Teacher: How many inches are there in a ruler?

Norma: 12.

Teacher: How many inches are there in a yardstick?

Norma: 36.

Teacher: How many feet are there in a yardstick?

Norma: 1.

Ms. Cortes notices that Norma has some sense of the number of inches represented by each tool—the ruler and the yardstick—but may not be visualizing how either of these tools represents feet or how all three measures—inches, feet, and yards—are related.

I reflected more on what Norma does know. Norma feels comfortable dealing with all inches, all feet, or all yards and can measure using those units to arrive at an accurate answer. She can tell me that 36 inches is three groups of 12 inches. As long as the measurement units are kept the same, Norma doesn't lose track of her work.

I thought Norma understood what a yardstick was. She was able to explain where the yardstick started and where it ended, and she could tell me that a yardstick had 36 inches. But somehow, when it came to determining the number of feet in a yard, Norma came up with an answer of 1. This was consistent with her saying that she used the yardstick 100 times to measure 100 feet. I wondered what was confusing her.

I wondered if Norma viewed the relationship between inches and feet and between feet and yards as having anything to do with multiplication and division. We had just finished a multiplication and division unit, so I knew that Norma might have this knowledge available to help her understand the problem.

I wrote 1 foot = 12 inches. I looked at her for approval, and she nodded in agreement.

Teacher: How many inches are in 2 feet?

Norma: 36.

I wait, thinking she might self-correct, but there is no response.

Teacher: Norma, if 1 foot is 12 inches, will 2 feet be 36 inches? Is 36 the double of 12?

Norma: Oh, no! It's 24.

I wrote 2 feet = 24 inches.

Teacher: How about 3 feet?

Norma: 24 + 12 . . . 36!

Teacher: So how many feet are in a yard?

Norma: 3.

Norma seemed to be able to find the number of inches in 2 feet and 3 feet by thinking about multiples of 12. I was surprised that she could then use the knowledge that 3 feet = 36 inches to determine the number of feet in a yard. Did Norma truly understand that 3 feet equals 1 yard or was she just answering mechanically?

The class came to an end. I spent some time thinking about what my next steps should be. I decided to next give her problems that focus on the multiplication relationship between feet and yards:

- There are 9 yards of cork on the floor. We have to cut the yards into strips that are 1-foot long. How many 1-foot strips can we make from each yard? How many 1-foot strips will we have in all?
- Some students measured their classroom in feet. The length of the room was 63 *feet.* Since there are 3 feet in 1 yard, how many *yards* long is their classroom?
- There are 3 feet in 1 yard. How many feet are there in 25 yards?

I can encourage Norma to model the problems using rulers and yardsticks. I want her to see the problems as both multiplication/division and measurement. Sometimes students see measurement problems like these simply as a conversion procedure—something they should just know, rather than something they can figure out. They do not realize that they are working with equal groups as they do when solving multiplication and division problems.

Although Norma seemed able to measure 100 feet using a yardstick, Ms. Cortes realized that Norma was not able to coordinate inches, feet, and yards. She questions Norma to find out what she does understand about measurement and what information she has about multiplication that might help her successfully group measurement units. Using this information as a starting point, Ms. Cortes begins to develop a plan to help Norma.

Questions for Discussion

1. **What does Norma understand about measurement? What aspects of measurement does she seem to be struggling with?**
2. **Ms. Cortes decides to have Norma solve a few multiplication/division problems to help her work on understanding the 3:1 relationship of feet to yards. What else could Ms. Cortes do to help Norma develop a better sense of measurement?**
3. **What confusions about measurement have your students had? What accommodations have you developed to help them develop a better understanding of measurement?**

Accommodations in an Inclusion Classroom: Silhouettes of Cube Buildings

All teachers are faced with the task of making the curriculum meaningful for students. Teachers of students with Individualized Education Plans have a particularly challenging task of providing access to mathematical concepts and tasks for the students with whom they work. This is true for John Ryder, a teacher of a class in which more than half of the students have documented special needs, including cerebral palsy, vision/depth perception difficulties, Asperger's syndrome, and behavioral and attention deficit issues. Whether or not you have this range of special education students in your classroom, you may find that Mr. Ryder's accommodations are relevant to a range of needs that you encounter with your own students.

Here are Mr. Ryder's thoughts as he prepares for a lesson that involves drawing a silhouette of a cube building. He thinks about the challenges his students may face and how he can best support them.

Moving between three-dimensional (3-D) shapes and two-dimensional (2-D) representations of these shapes has typically proven difficult for some students in my class. Making mental pictures of images can be very difficult. After my first few years using *Investigations,* I learned that it is beneficial to engage students in mental math activities early in the school year, well before they are faced with the task of making representations of cube buildings. I have found that mental imaging helps many students visualize quantities and shapes so that they can then manipulate them.

When thinking about the math activity of drawing silhouettes of a building made from cubes, I thought that Steven might have difficulty moving between 2-D and 3-D images due to his poor depth perception. He might also have some difficulty putting the cubes together because of difficulties with gross motor management. I considered asking him to use stickers or to alternate the colors in his structure. I also thought about enlarging the picture for him. After a great deal of reflection, I decided not to provide an accommodation for him at this time but to see how he does on his own. I knew I would be prepared if it appeared that Steven did need some additional support. I planned on working closely with him to monitor his progress and to offer an accommodation if needed.

I also thought about Donna, who is new to the class and new to *Investigations.* She typically has a lot of difficulty when working with activities that involve numbers. For these geometry activities, I anticipate that she will not have as much difficulty, but I will need to watch her closely.

Francesca, Nathan, Laura, and Carl are four students in my class who are very strong mathematicians. They should challenge themselves during this activity but probably will need coaxing to do this. These students tend to do the bare minimum to complete the activity. I'll need to watch them and be ready to ask them probing questions when they inform me that they have completed the activity.

After the lesson, Mr. Ryder reflected on how his students approached the activity. He used what he learned to help prepare for the next day's activity, Drawing All Three Views.

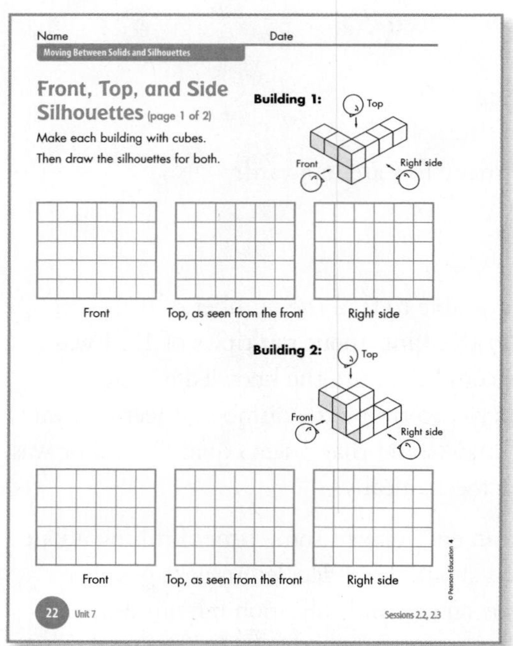
Name Date

Moving Between Solids and Silhouettes

Front, Top, and Side Silhouettes (page 1 of 2)

Make each building with cubes.
Then draw the silhouettes for both.

Building 1: Top, Front, Right side

Front | Top, as seen from the front | Right side

Building 2: Top, Front, Right side

Front | Top, as seen from the front | Right side

22 Unit 7 Sessions 2.2, 2.3

© Pearson Education 4

▲ **Student Activity Book, p. 22 (Unit 7)**

At the beginning of class, I reminded students about the strategies they used yesterday. I asked Carl, Francesca, Nathan and Laura to try to draw the silhouettes without building the 3-D structure with cubes. I also asked these students to construct the 3-D building with the least number of cubes and with the greatest number of cubes, while still attending to the image on their student sheet. I wanted these students to visualize the various perspectives in their heads, and I felt as though they could benefit from the challenge.

Yesterday, Donna was having some difficulty orienting her building to the one that I was using. For Donna, I continued modeling ways to turn the cube building and the practice of getting down to eye level with the cube building resting on the table. I later observed Donna, kneeling on the floor with her cube building in her line of sight. This was a great strategy for her to isolate the view that she was directly working on. These concrete actions helped Donna better visualize multiple views when she constructed her own cube building.

After observing Steven yesterday, I decided he needed several accommodations to help him successfully complete the assignment for next time. For this activity, I created a cube building just for him that was less complex. Also, I made sure to enlarge the picture, enhance the contrast, and tape the picture to a slant board that he typically uses for reading. I also had Steven use the large graph paper instead of the small graph paper used by other students. Another accommodation that I made was tracing over the lines on the graph paper and then photocopying this image so that the lines were a bit darker and easier for him to trace. I then encouraged him to alternate colors (dark and bright colors) when constructing his building, which later helped him draw the silhouettes more precisely. He continued to have some difficulties constructing the cube building accurately; however, these accommodations allowed him to work on this activity independently, which was a milestone in itself.

Accommodations are not something that you prepare once at the beginning of the lesson. As Mr. Ryder shows, accommodations need to be continually anticipated and planned through thoughtful attention to how each student approaches a task.

Questions for Discussion

1. **Mr. Ryder writes about six students in this case. What did he know about each student before starting this activity? How did he use this knowledge to determine beforehand the possible accommodations for each student?**

2. **As he observed them during the activity, what decisions did he make about accommodations to support and/or challenge each student?**

3. **In what ways do you consider the individual needs of your students when planning and presenting lessons? How do you use what you have learned about how a student approaches a task to help you meet his/her needs during subsequent activities? Think about one or two particular students to answer these questions.**

Providing Modifications and Checking Assumptions: How Many 4s Are in 1,500?

Students in Molly Levy's fourth-grade class have been working with factors of multiples of 100. Mrs. Levy feels that some of the students in her classroom would benefit from an additional challenge as a result of their strong mathematical grasp of the factors of 100 and of the first few multiples of 100 (200, 300, 400). Consequently, for these students, Mrs. Levy modifies the problem from "How many 4s are in 100 (200, 300)?" to "How many 4s are in 1,500?"

The following is an excerpt of Mrs. Levy's account of a discussion of the modified problem with some of these students:

Teacher: Would 4 be a factor of 1,500?

Michael: Yes, because it is a factor of 100. $4 \times 25 = 100$. So then you keep on doing that a lot of times.

Teacher: How many times?

Michael: Umm . . . [He pauses and is clearly having some difficulty figuring this out.]

Teacher: I am going to stop you. What's going on in your head? What are you thinking about?

Michael: I'm trying to think how many 4s there would be in 1,500. I'm not sure if this is right, but I'm trying to do 1,500 $\times$ 4. No, times 25. There are 25 fours in 100.

Teacher: So we've got 25, we've got 4, we've got 1,500 . . . What are the relationships?

Natalie: In each 100 there are four 25s. If you're figuring out how many there would be, you could do 1,000 times 25 and 500 times 25.

Ned has his hand up throughout this discussion, but I chose not to call on him because I think he sees the problem with

Michael and Natalie's reasoning. I am hoping others will realize that the answers given by both Michael and Natalie aren't reasonable. All of the students working on this problem seem quite satisfied with pursuing Michael's idea. They are focused on how to solve 25 × 1,500, not how many 4s are in 1,500.

The conversation continues with Michael who says that 25 times 1,000 equals 25,000, so there are 25,000 fours in 1,000. The others (except for Ned) are just sitting there waiting to move on. I am amazed that no one is questioning Michael's statement. They've lost sight of the quantities and the relationships. What they can demonstrate so well with the smaller numbers is lost in working with such a large number. When I do call on Ned, he offers another viewpoint:

Ned: In the beginning I had a different way to solve it. A lot of people were thinking about multiplying by 4 or multiplying by 25, but that would completely take you off track because if you're trying to find how many fours are in something, then you divide the thing by 4. I would have divided 1,500 by 4.

Despite Ned's statement, students continue to struggle with the problem, adding zeros to the ends of numbers, building charts similar to the 300 chart they've been using, and using other concrete strategies to help them solve the problem.

As I think about this session, I am puzzled. I wanted to push these students to prove a generalization they had made that all the factors of 100 are factors of all the hundreds numbers. What a surprise I got! I am left with a number of questions.

- How is it possible that most students didn't question Michael's assertion that there are 25,000 fours in 1,500?
- How did they slip away from their usual good thinking about numbers and their relationships? Did they lose their number sense because of the size of the numbers? Were they just tired after more than an hour of math class?
- How can I use Ned's statement about dividing by 4 to help the other students understand the error in their thinking? How can I help them connect Ned's idea to their strategy of starting with the number of 4s in 100?

The most amazing understandings and misunderstandings arise even from my strongest math students.

As Mrs. Levy discovered, students who present themselves as being capable and motivated math students still need repeated experiences and support exploring number relationships, particularly when working in new contexts or on more difficult problems. Mrs. Levy now has additional information about the students with whom she worked during this lesson. This information will inform the decisions she makes on how to best to support these students in further work with factors and multiples of 100. It may also contribute to her thinking about how to support and extend the work of all her students.

Questions for Discussion

1. **Find the solution to the problem "How many 4s are in 1,500?" yourself. Then think about what knowledge you used to solve it.**
2. **What did the students in Mrs. Levy's group understand about applying their knowledge of factors of 100 to finding factors of multiples of 100? What confused them?**
3. **What was surprising to Mrs. Levy about the misunderstandings that became apparent during this discussion? How can she build understanding based on what the students do understand?**
4. **Think of a time that you were surprised by the misunderstandings of students who often need more challenge. What concepts proved more puzzling for them than you expected? What experiences did you provide to help them sort through their confusion?**

The Case of Maura: Now That I Know the Exact Answer I Can Figure Out the Estimate: Helping a Student Understand Estimation

Although students have had experience with estimating by fourth grade, some learners still struggle with how to determine a reasonable estimate. This is the case for Maura, a fourth-grade student in Ms. Lloyd's classroom. In this case, Ms. Lloyd talks to Maura to try to get a sense of what she understands and does not understand about estimating.

One of my students, Maura, is really struggling with estimation. Her responses are far off and often do not make sense. By early April, we had worked on a variety of estimation problems and had various tools, including number lines and 100 and 300 charts, to help visualize these problems. Still Maura seemed totally perplexed by the idea of estimating. I know that her computational fluency is shaky. I decided to sit down and talk with her to see if I could get a better sense of what she does and does not understand about estimating. Maura was working on estimating the answer to 14 × 30 when I joined her.

Teacher: This question asked you to estimate 14 × 30. Your answer is 12,000. Show me how you got that answer.

Maura: Well, I'm really not sure. I know that multiplying is more than one of the same number. So, more than one, or in this case 30 of 14 is a lot. But, I don't know exactly how much.

Maura seemed to be struggling with larger numbers. I decided to reduce one of the numbers. I wondered if she was intimidated by the size of the numbers, or if she even had a sense of how large a multiple of 10 might be.

Teacher: With estimating, you don't need the exact answer, but you want an answer that's pretty close. Let's make the numbers smaller. What if I asked you to estimate the answer to 14 × 3? [Maura starts to count and calculate on her fingers.] What are you doing? Say it out loud so I can follow you.

Maura: I'm breaking apart the number. Fourteen is 10 and 4, so 3 tens is [nodding her head as she counts] 30. Then, what's left? Four. Then [looking down at her paper] 4 times 3 is 12, so then I add the parts together. That's 42.

It seemed that Maura was trying to keep all the numbers in her head, as she's seen other students do. That could be part of the problem.

Teacher: Yes, that's the exact answer. What could you do to estimate?

Maura: Now that I know the exact answer, I can figure out the estimate.

Teacher: You're saying that you can't get a sense of how big the number is?

Maura: No, I can't. How do people estimate? I mean, what numbers are they looking at?

Teacher: So you're saying that it's a mystery how to figure out numbers to use to estimate?

Maura: Yes!

Teacher: Good question. Let's solve that mystery. Let's take one of these numbers, 14. You broke the number up into 10 and 4. What else could you do with 14?

Maura: I remember about rounding to an easier number to use.

Teacher: Show me how you might round 14 on a number line.

Maura: [Sketches a line with arrows on either end, puts 10 on one end, 20 on the other, with 14 almost in the middle.] Fourteen is right about here.

Teacher: Take me on a trip along this number line. Tell me what numbers we're seeing and passing. For example, why put 10 and 20 on the line?

Maura: Well, 14 is between 10 and 20. I could put the number 15 right here because that's halfway between 10 and 20. Fourteen is one less than 15. I could round 14 down to 10, and yet it's really close to 15. Fifteen is a good number to use because it ends in five, and I'm really good with numbers that end in five.

Teacher: So, when you see the number 14, you could use either 10 or 15 as a landmark or an easy-to-use number.

From Maura's response, I could tell that she could use the number line and was able to point out important information like midpoint amounts and proximity. She could also correctly describe distances from certain points and how and why multiples of five are useful.

Teacher: When would you use 10 and when would you use 15?

Maura: Ten is easy to multiply with, and I can keep it in my head. But 15 is closer, which would make my estimate closer to the exact answer. So when should I use either?

Teacher: Good question, Maura. Which can you use and keep more easily in your head? It sounds as if you're aware that 10 is further away from 14 than 15 is. So, when you get an estimated answer, you can remember that if you use 15, your answer will be closer to the exact answer than if you use 10.

From our conversation I learned that Maura had more understanding than her work had previously indicated, but she still needed to solve the mystery of arriving at an estimate. I had a hunch that Maura was not rounding numbers but trying to use the given numbers to quickly (and erroneously) arrive at an answer.

Teacher: So, when you look at the numbers in an estimating problem, what are you doing?

Maura: I'm trying to solve the problem.

Teacher: How?

Maura: If I have to multiply, then I do that.

Teacher: Are you rounding to friendly numbers first?

Maura: No, I'm just adding or multiplying or doing whatever the problem says to do.

Because I know Maura and have a trusting relationship with her, I asked this next question in a friendly way.

Teacher: Are you looking around and seeing other kids doing this fast and you want to be fast, too?

Maura: [grinning] Yeah!

Teacher: You know that they're changing the exact numbers into friendly or landmark numbers. Did you know that?

Maura: They *are*?

Teacher: Yes, they need to do that, just as you and I need to. They aren't mysteriously multiplying those complicated numbers in their heads and coming up with answers. They're looking at the numbers and finding friendly numbers for them, then multiplying.

Maura: Oh!

Teacher: So, how about if I give you a little practice finding friendly or landmark numbers? You seem pretty sharp with that.

Maura: I am. I know how to do that. Now I understand better.

As a social learner, Maura had been observing her classmates work through these assignments, but even with all the "share out loud with your math partner" opportunities, Maura had not necessarily picked up on what other students were doing. I have noticed her not always paying attention to her partner's explanation. It makes sense that if she didn't quite get what's going on, she would have difficulty following her partner's explanation. The individual conversation with her was critical in identifying with her what she knows and what she didn't understand.

In this case, Ms. Lloyd illustrates how powerful a one-on-one conversation with a student can be. Ms. Lloyd is aware that Maura is struggling with estimation but is not clear on what aspect of estimating is confusing her. By talking with Maura and asking her a series of questions, Ms. Lloyd comes to understand what Maura does and does not know about estimation. What she has learned from their conversation will guide her next steps with Maura.

Questions for Discussion

1. **What did Maura understand about estimating? What was she confused about?**

2. **Which of Ms. Lloyd's questions seemed to be the most helpful in sorting out the confusion Maura was having? Are there other questions she might have asked or contexts she might have used to help Maura understand estimation?**

3. **What next steps would you put in place for Maura or students like her?**

4. **From your own experience, when do you decide to work one on one with a student during a lesson? How do you decide when sharing with a partner is not helping students move ahead in their understanding?**

The Case of Kevin and Dejara: Multiplying by Multiples of 10

Sarah Peck is a math resource teacher. In this case, she works with a group of fourth graders who are stuck using inefficient multiplication strategies. Realizing that their lack of understanding about a major mathematical idea is holding them back, she provides a learning experience that enables them to work through the roadblock. Following the lesson, she notices a change in the students' mathematical understanding as well as their attitude about math.

I work with a small group of fourth graders once a week. Kevin has been very resistant to trying to understand the mathematics behind our work, and Dejara is constantly distracting others and is easily distracted herself. It is difficult to work with them in a group, even a small group, as they have been reluctant to participate or work to make sense of the mathematics we do. I am convinced that their reactions come from the gaps in their mathematical understanding and the feelings of inadequacy that result. Indeed, last week Dejara referred to herself as stupid when she had trouble with a problem.

Their class was working on double-digit by single-digit multiplication. Kevin and Dejara both showed an understanding of multiplication and were able to solve the problems, but they didn't have efficient strategies. On her homework, Dejara used repeated addition most of the time. Kevin broke the numbers into tens and ones but didn't multiply by *multiples* of 10. For example,

Dehara's Strategy		*Kevin's Strategy*	
$6 \times 32 = 192$		$6 \times 32 = 192$	
32	32	$6 \times 10 = 60$	
32	32	$6 \times 10 = 60$	
+32	+32	$6 \times 10 = 60$	
96	96	$6 \times 2 = 12$	
$90 + 90 = 180$		60	
$6 + 6 = +12$		60	180
	192	+60	+ 12
		180	192

Since I was unsure what they understood about multiplying by multiples of 10, I designed a lesson to try to find out.

I started by asking them to construct the 7s table on their papers. As they finished, I put a column of problems with 70 on their papers:

$7 \times 1 = 7$	$70 \times 1 =$
$7 \times 2 = 14$	$70 \times 2 =$
$7 \times 3 = 21$	$70 \times 3 =$
$7 \times 4 = 28$	$70 \times 4 =$
$7 \times 5 = 35$	$70 \times 5 =$
$7 \times 6 = 42$	$70 \times 6 =$
$7 \times 7 = 49$	$70 \times 7 =$
$7 \times 8 = 56$	$70 \times 8 =$
$7 \times 9 = 63$	$70 \times 9 =$
$7 \times 10 = 70$	$70 \times 10 =$

I asked them to solve as many of the 70s problems as they could in their heads, just writing down the answers. I told them they could use paper and pencil or a calculator when they got stuck. Calculators were also available for checking answers.

Teacher: How are the two columns different from each other?

Kevin: You're just doing 70 instead of 7, so you put a 0 on the answer.

Teacher: Why do you put on a 0?

Kevin: That's how it works!

Dejara: [nodding in agreement] You're not supposed to say you're adding a 0 because you're not really adding. So you just say you're putting on the 0.

Teacher: Well, it's certainly getting you the right answers! I wonder why it works. How does putting a 0 on the 7 change it?

Kevin: It makes it a 70.

Teacher: What's happened to the 7 part?

Kevin: It's now 7 tens.

Teacher: Exactly! It went from being 7 ones to being 7 tens. We've actually multiplied the 7 by 10 when we do that.

Kevin: Is that what happens when you put on the 0? Are you always multiplying by 10?

We tried various numbers on the calculator to see if it worked with large numbers too, and it did. This was new information.

We looked back at the 70s problems to see what else we could discover.

Dejara: 70 × 6 is just like 7 × 6 but with a 0.

Teacher: Let's start with 7 × 6 = 42. When I change it to 70 × 6, what have I done to the 7?

Kevin: You times the 7 by 10.

Teacher: So what will I have to do to the answer [42]?

Kevin: [after a long pause] Times the 42 by 10?

Dejara: Yes, it's going to be 420.

Teacher: Whatever I do to change the problem, I also have to do to change the answer to keep them equal. [I make a mental note that this is another idea we need to explore more.]

Next, I give them four challenge problems to work on. Calculators are available for checking but not for solving. The four challenge problems are as follows:

3 × 70 = ____
30 × 7 = ____
70 × 60 = ____
28 × 7 = ____

They solved them independently and then shared their ideas. For a change, they were really listening to each other. They both solved the first two using the basic factor pair (3 × 7) and putting a 0 on the end. There was some confusion about the third problem (70 × 60), so we broke it into steps:

Teacher: What fact will you start with?

Dejara: 7 × 6 = 42

I wrote it on the board.

Teacher: How does the 7 change?

Dejara: You multiply it by 10 to get to 70.

I changed the 7 to 70 on the board.

Teacher: How will that change your answer?

Kevin: It's 420.

I changed the 42 to 420 on the board.

Teacher: How does the 6 change?

Kevin: You times it by 10.

I changed the 6 to 60 on the board.

Teacher: How will that change your answer?

Kevin: [his face lights up] Oh, I get it. It will be 4,200. That's easy!

Dejara: I love this because we can do hard problems.

Teacher: Sometimes if you break the problem apart and think about it in steps, it does make the problem easy to solve. How can you break the last problem [28 × 7] apart to make it easy to solve?

Dejara isn't sure, but Kevin breaks it into tens and ones as he did on his homework. This time, however, he doesn't break 20 into 2 tens.

Kevin: You just break the 28 into 20 and 8 and times both by 7! That's really easy . . . except I have to figure out 8 × 7. Oh wait, I already did. It's right here. [He points to the 7s table he constructed at the beginning of the lesson.]

We tried a couple more two-digit by one-digit problems. They were excited by how easy they were to solve.

Teacher: So if you had your homework problems to do now, would you do them differently?

Kevin: You bet!

I gave him the six homework problems to do over again and he whipped through them, using his new idea about multiplying by multiples of 10. Dejara used a different strategy for the first problem, 8×22. She solved 4×22 and doubled it. This was the same strategy she used on her homework, and it is a good one for this problem. However, I asked her if she could also do it another way, and she broke the 22 apart into 20 and 2 and solved it correctly that way.

When they finished redoing their homework, they asked me to give them more hard problems. When our time was up, they begged to stay. When I said that wasn't possible, they asked if they could come during recess. Who are these new math lovers? Certainly not the Kevin and Dejara I've had before. They did come during recess and continued working on one-digit by two-, three-, even four-digit problems. They felt empowered and smart and couldn't wait to show their work to their classroom teacher and their parents.

As we wrapped up at the end of recess, we talked briefly about what made these problems easy.

Kevin: You just have to know how to multiply by 10.

Teacher: Well yes, but you also need the factor pairs we have been learning, like 7×6.

Dejara: But you don't have to learn everything. Like you don't have to learn 37×6. You just break the 37 into 30 and 7.

We made a major breakthrough today, not only in the students' understanding of the math, but also in their attitude about math. Kevin and Dejara are beginning to see that math can make sense, or rather that *they* can make sense of math. They *want* to practice, to solidify what they are beginning to understand about multiplying by multiples of 10. They are focused, listening to each other, and taking risks. Wow! What a difference!

What caused this change? I have to remind myself that although it is December, I have only met with them ten times. We are still getting comfortable with each other. This was only the second time we worked on multidigit multiplication. I was able to identify a big mathematical idea holding them back. They understood multiplying by 10 at some level, but they didn't know how to use that information in their solving strategies. They also didn't really understand what putting a 0 on the end meant or how they could expand the idea to multiplying by multiples of 10. As they looked across their threshold of understanding, they saw something powerful that was within their grasp. They wanted to own it.

I have no illusions that they've mastered this idea, but they are certainly in a different place than they were last week. I'm sure they will move in and out of using multiples of 10 in their strategies as they come to own the idea. How will they approach tonight's homework?

Realizing that two of her students were stuck using inefficient multiplication strategies, Ms. Peck created a learning experience that gave the students a chance to experience the power of multiplying by tens. Now able to see past the notion of "you just add a zero on the end," the students approached multiplication with both excitement and a newfound confidence.

Questions for Discussion

1. **What did Kevin and Dejara each understand about multiplication at the beginning of this case? What did they not understand?**

2. **How did learning about multiplying multiples of 10 help each of them move toward more powerful strategies for solving multiplication problems?**

3. **What commonalities do you see between Ms. Peck's work with Kevin and Dejara and Ms. Lloyd's work with Maura in the previous case?**

4. **Think about one or two of your students who are struggling and also lack confidence. How can you build their confidence while offering them experiences to improve their understanding?**

Language and Representation

Creating a Supportive Environment for Hedson

Ms. Lloyd, a fourth-grade teacher, is determined to include Hedson, an English Language Learner with significant academic and social challenges, in all aspects of the classroom. In this case, she shares how she creates a supportive environment for Hedson that enables him to share his ideas with the class.

Hedson is one of my students. I have made great efforts this year to include him in all aspects of our math class. He has an extensive and detailed Individualized Education Plan that notes significant attention issues, language challenges, and delays. He is a second language learner, but he also seems to have word retrieval, usage, and expressive language problems in both languages. He reads considerably below grade level.

Hedson loves math. He says it is his favorite subject and is more diligent about bringing in his math homework than any other homework. Because reading is difficult for him, I have noticed that when completing worksheets, he will skip over text and seek meaning from the numbers themselves. Hedson is also preoccupied with the difficult situation in his country of origin; with prompting from me, he has talked and written about it. Despite all this, Hedson tries each and every day to participate in math class.

I have made several accommodations to help Hedson be successful in math class. I have found that he works best with just one partner and have been pairing him with another English Language Learner. The two boys seem to have similar ways of describing numbers and quantities and have been working well together. Because reading is a challenge for Hedson, I have created worksheets with less text. I make boxed-in spaces with simple labels to make it easier for him to follow the directions. This helps to eliminate any confusing or distracting information. I always seat Hedson near the board and near me. Finally, I provide Hedson with a lot of eye contact during class discussions. He understands my looks as either "Focus," "Are you with me?" or "Does this make sense to you?" I will put my hand on his to show my support. I have found that he often puts his hand on top of mine and keeps it there, possibly as an anchor to help him stay focused. I have found that these accommodations have helped Hedson to participate accurately and seriously in math class.

My students have been working on using the number line to practice addition and subtraction. I decided to begin math class by reviewing the homework from the previous night. I asked Hedson to start our homework discussion. The problem was 1,000 − 489.

Teacher: Hedson, what is the problem we are solving now?

Hedson pauses for about 30 seconds. He looks down at his paper, pencil in hand. The class is quiet. They know him and act on our classroom culture's expectation that every student gets the time she or he needs.

Teacher: We are on the first one. Tell me the numbers to write on the board. [A student's hand goes up.] Hands down, please. It's Hedson's turn. He knows.

Hedson looks up at me. I nod back at him, beckoning his speech with my eyes, chalk in hand, ready to write. My body is calm. I will wait with him. And so will the class.

Hedson: I think it's — um, um. I think it's, I think you say it like this: one, one [nods, pushing his chin way down], one thousand is the first number.

Teacher: Like this? [I write 1,000 on the board and then look calmly in his eyes.]

Hedson: Yes, like that.

Teacher: Okay. What's next?

Hedson: You take the other number. [He looks up at me.]

Teacher: What is the number? I don't have the sheet. You do. Read it to us.

Hedson: Four, four [stops]. It's four, four hundred eight, then an 8, then a 9.

Teacher: Tell me the number all together.

I nod and wait, maintaining eye contact with him. My body language is patient and calm. Other students have settled down and wait with me.

Hedson: I think, I think it's four hundred [nods a few times], four hundred and eighty-nine. [Nods again more forcefully.]

Teacher: You're sure. [I nod now and smile slightly.]

Hedson: [smiling back] Yes, I'm sure.

Teacher: Now, tell me what to do, what to write.

Hedson: You make, like one of those. [Draws a horizontal line in the air.] Like this.

Teacher: Tell me what you want me to write.

Hedson: A line. Like this. [Draws a line in the air again.]

I nod and wait. He continues . . .

Hedson: Then, on one side, write one thousand. [Points with his finger from his chair.]

Teacher: On the left here or on the right? [I point to each side as I say the word.]

Hedson: On the left? One thousand. Yes.

Ms. Lloyd: [I write the number followed by the minus sign that Hedson indicated: 1,000] Now what do I do?

Hedson: On the other side [points] you write the smaller number. Four hundred . . . four hundred eighty-nine. [Squints, points.]

Teacher: Here? [I point with my finger to the right side.]

Hedson: Yes. There. [Nods.]

1,000 − 489

I wasn't sure if Hedson had solved the problem correctly, but I decided to give him a chance and see if he could make sense of the numbers.

Teacher: About what would the answer be?

Hedson: [Hesitating, repeating the numbers slowly] 1,000 − 489. [He looks again at me for assurance.]

Teacher: What number is 489 close to?

Hedson: 500.

I nod at him and smile.

Teacher: How does that help you?

Hedson: 500 is easy.

Teacher: So what would 1,000 − 500 be?

Hedson: [with a smile] 500.

I smile back and continue.

Teacher: So about what would 1,000 − 489 be?

Hedson: A little more than 500.

Teacher: [to the class] Does everyone agree with Hedson? [Murmurs of yes and a series of nods go through the class.]

I knew I'd taken a great deal of time to help Hedson through his presentation. By doing this, I reinforced our class's value that every student can and will participate in sharing. Everyone gets a chance to contribute his or her ideas to the class, and the class gets a chance to listen and learn from one another's thinking. By questioning Hedson, I was also making sure that my other students who are struggling understood his strategy.

As I stayed with Hedson during his presentation, I was also watching the other students for any signs of disrespect. I didn't see any. Because I have paired Hedson with a variety of students throughout the year, the class has experience working with him and is aware of his style and strengths. They also know about my fierce and articulated advocacy of all students. Though Hedson can become frustrated and lose confidence at times when he has difficulty listening or expressing himself, he also likes to discuss math and is quite accurate in his calculations. Hedson forces those students who would otherwise breeze through an activity with little reflection to reflect on their own words and written feedback. He makes them slow down and listen to him.

Hedson reminds me of how important it is to keep gesturing as I speak and to clearly write out the steps to the strategies we are discussing as well as talking about them. That way, students with directionality confusions, with visual and auditory processing challenges, and general distractions can and will get use out of each and every math class. Every class is a language class as well as a math class.

Sharing ideas in a class discussion can be a stressful venture for any student. It can be particularly challenging for the English Language Learner, particularly one with language issues that are manifested in the first language as well and go beyond those encountered by other English Language Learners. With this in mind, Ms. Lloyd has taken many steps to make the classroom a supportive environment for Hedson. She is careful to use hand gestures and a variety of verbal instructions to improve communication. Throughout Hedson's presentation, she encourages him by using verbal and nonverbal cues. Finally, she has created a community of learners that appears to understand one another's other's strengths and weaknesses and is able to support one another's learning.

Questions for Discussion

1. **Ms. Lloyd uses many verbal and nonverbal cues throughout the exchange with Hedson to both encourage and support Hedson's sharing with the class. What does she do to make him feel comfortable in the classroom while at the same time supporting his mathematical growth?**
2. **What does Ms. Lloyd learn from working with Hedson? How does the class benefit from listening to Hedson?**
3. **What are ways you make your mathematics classroom a supportive environment for English Language Learners? How do you structure sharing time to make it comfortable for all learners?**

Helping Students Make Sense of Penny Jar Problems: Using an Array Representation

In this case, Norma Bell's students have been working on a problem from Unit 9, Penny Jars and Plant Growth. *In this problem, 7 pennies are in the jar to start and 4 pennies are added each round. Students are asked to find and record how many pennies are in the jar for rounds 1 through 7 and also for rounds 10, 15, and 20. Students began with a variety of strategies to solve this problem, and most of the class understands that they can multiply the number of the round by 4 to get the number of pennies in the jar and then add the 7 pennies that were there at the start. However, Ms. Bell is concerned about a small group of students who are unable to go from round 7 to round 10 without calculating the intervening steps. She writes about her work helping these students visualize the problem and how it relates to the expression* $(4 \times 10) + 7$.

Round	Total Number of Pennies
Start	7
1	11
2	15
3	19
4	23
5	27
6	31
7	35
10	
15	
20	

Some students were stuck on adding on each round and had no strategy for skipping rounds. Others were trying to follow the multiplication strategies they saw during discussion, but they couldn't explain how the strategy related to the situation. That is, they might write $(4 \times 10) + 7$, but they couldn't explain what the 4×10 meant or why it worked. The lack of connection to the situation showed up in their errors as well. When someone wrote $(7 \times 10) + 4$, these students had trouble figuring out which of the two number sentences represented "7 pennies to start; add 4 pennies each round."

I decided to return to the pennies and the jar with a small group of students and help them visualize what was happening and how it related to the number sentences. I also hoped that the work with visualizing would move some students from thinking about the problem additively to thinking multiplicatively. Although the situation uses the term *add,* students need to multiply to figure out how many pennies are in the jar without counting every round. This is a huge shift for some fourth graders. I felt the model of a jar they added pennies to only reinforced the idea of adding on. So I used a different model this time, one where they could see all of the pennies, with the added pennies arranged in an array.

I drew a paper Penny Jar and had chips to represent pennies.

Abdul picked a Penny Jar situation card: 4 pennies to start. Add 3 pennies each round.

We put the start pennies on the paper Penny Jar at the bottom, and I drew a line above them. Then students took turns adding the next rounds, lining them up neatly in rows. After each round I drew a line above the pennies. When the jar was partly full, I asked how many rounds we had and how many pennies were in the jar.

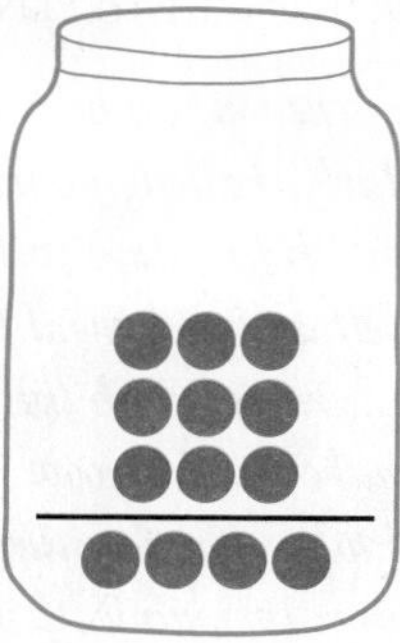

Teacher: How many rounds do we have?

Caitlin: 4, no 3 — you don't count the start pennies.

Teacher: How many pennies are in the jar?

Esther: 13. $4 + 3 = 7$; $7 + 3 = 10$; $10 + 3 = 13$. I started with the start number and just added 3s.

Teacher: Did anyone solve it a different way?

Courtney: $3 \times 3 = 9$. And we started with 4 pennies, so plus 4 equals 13 [$9 + 4 = 13$].

Teacher: Show us the 3×3 in the jar.

Courtney points to the 3 rows of 3 pennies. We continue filling the jar.

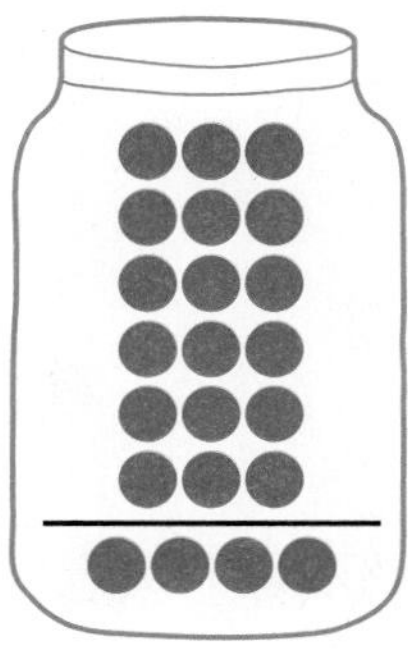

Teacher: How many pennies do we have now?

Matt: 22. We have six rounds of three: 3, 6, 9, 12, 15, 18, and then 4 more is 22.

Teacher: How many pennies have we put in the jar, not counting what we started with?

Daniel: 18.

Teacher: How many did we start with?

Esther: 4.

Teacher: How many in the jar?

Esther: 22.

We did a number of situations together, talking about where we could see the start pennies and where the added pennies were. We also talked about how to find out how many pennies were added. Some found the array model useful in knowing what to multiply. Others continued to think about the situation as $3 + 3 + 3$. . . . I would then ask, "Is there another way to write that?" One of my goals was to have students see these two parts of the situation: the start pennies and the added pennies. Further, I hoped that the array formed by the pennies in the jar would move them to use multiplication in solving.

As these students returned to work independently or with a partner, some carried these ideas into their work. Since we have been using arrays to think about multiplication in other contexts, these students could now use the image of the array to think about how multiplication applies to the Penny Jar. But others reverted to adding each round. They will need to explore these relationships further.

By drawing a jar and representing both the starting pennies and those added each round, Ms. Bell drew on the students' work with arrays in multiplication to create a model to help students visualize the action in this problem. This model helped students understand why multiplying the number of rounds by the number of pennies added each time, then adding the starting number, results in the total number of pennies in the jar. Although not all students were ready to draw on this model, Ms. Bell was successful in moving some students forward and will continue to work with the others.

Questions for Discussion

1. **How did Ms. Bell's model help the students move from counting or adding to multiplying?**
2. **What additional support can Ms. Bell provide to those students who were not yet ready to draw on this model? What experiences might they need to help them understand the multiplicative structure of this problem?**
3. **Can you think of a time in your classroom when a representation helped students make sense of a mathematical problem or idea with which they were struggling or when you might have used a representation to do so?**

PART 8

Scope and Sequence

LOOKING BACK AT:

Grade 3

Grade 4

LOOKING FORWARD TO:

Grade 5

Each strand is labeled with a grade level.

The content is organized around five strands.

The strands are divided into Math Emphases.

The Math Emphases may be covered in one or more units. The Math Emphases are further subdivided into Math Focus Points.

GRADE 4

Number and Operations

Whole Number Operations Understanding and working with an array model of multiplication

Unit 1 Math Focus Points

- Using arrays to model multiplication situations
- Breaking an array into parts to find the product represented by the array
- Using arrays to find factors of 2-digit numbers
- Identifying features of numbers, including prime, square, and composite numbers

Whole Number Operations Reasoning about numbers and their factors

Unit 1 Math Focus Points

- Finding the multiples of a number by skip counting
- Determining whether one number is a factor or multiple of another
- Identifying the factors of a given number
- Identifying all the factors of 100
- Using knowledge of the factors of 100 to find factors of multiples of 100
- Using known multiplication combinations to find related multiplication combinations for a given product (e.g., if $4 \times 50 = 200$, then $8 \times 25 = 200$)
- Using representations to show that a factor of a number is also a factor of its multiples (e.g., if 25 is a factor of 100, then 25 is also a factor of 300)

GRADE 3

Number and Operations

The Base-Ten Number System Understanding the equivalence of one group and the discrete units that comprise it

Unit 1 Math Focus Points

- Recognizing and representing the place value of each digit in 2- and 3-digit numbers
- Using equivalencies among pennies, dimes, and dollars
- Finding different combinations of 100s, 10s, and 1s for a number and recognizing their equivalence (e.g., 1 hundred, 3 tens, and 7 ones equals 1 hundred, 2 tens, and 17 ones, or 13 tens and 7 ones)
- Recognizing and demonstrating the equivalence of one 100 to ten 10s and one 10 to ten 1s
- Recognizing and using coin equivalencies

Unit 3 Math Focus Points

- Constructing 1,000 from groups of 100
- Recognizing and representing the number of tens in 3-digit numbers
- Representing the structure of 3-digit numbers as being composed of 100s, 10s, and 1s
- Using the value of each place to make 2- and 3-digit numbers closest to 100

The Base-Ten Number System Extending knowledge of the number system to 1,000

Unit 3 Math Focus Points

- Reading, writing, and sequencing numbers to 1,000
- Using place value to determine the size of any number to 1,000

Unit 8 Math Focus Points

- Reading and writing numbers in the thousands

Computational Fluency Adding and subtracting accurately and efficiently

Unit 1 Math Focus Points

- Adding and subtracting multiples of 10
- Solving addition problems with 2-digit numbers by using strategies that involve breaking numbers apart by place or adding one number in parts
- Solving addition problems with 2-digit numbers that involve more than 10 ones in the ones place and explaining the effect on the sum
- Finding the difference between a 2-digit number and 100
- Adding pennies and dimes to sums up to $2.00
- Learning/reviewing addition combinations up to 10 + 10
- Using knowledge of place value to find pairs of 2-digit numbers that add to 100 or a number close to 100
- Using known pairs of 2-digit numbers that add to 100 to find related pairs that add to 100 or a number close to 100 (for example, 20 + 80 = 100, so 22 + 78 = 100)
- Estimating the sums of 2-digit numbers by using knowledge of place value and known combinations
- Finding combinations of coins that equal $1.00
- Using mathematical tools (cubes, 100 charts and grids, number lines) to solve problems and represent strategies

Unit 3 Math Focus Points

- Estimating the sums of 2- and 3-digit numbers using knowledge of place value and known combinations
- Finding pairs of numbers that add to 100
- Finding the difference between 2- and 3-digit numbers and 100
- Finding the difference between 3-digit numbers
- Solving addition problems with 2- and 3-digit numbers (to 400) by breaking numbers apart and recombining them
- Representing addition strategies
- Adding and subtracting multiples of 10 and 100
- Developing strategies for solving addition problems by focusing on how each strategy starts

- Gaining fluency with subtraction facts related to addition combinations up to $10 + 10$
- Using multiples of 100 as a landmark to solve subtraction problems
- Solving subtraction problems with 2- and 3-digit numbers (to 300) using strategies that involve either subtracting one number in parts, adding up, or subtracting back
- Finding the difference between two numbers by either adding or subtracting
- Reasoning about how increasing the numbers in a subtraction problem affects the difference

Unit 8 Math Focus Points

- Combining hundreds to numbers above 1,000
- Subtracting from multiples of 100
- Adding multiples of 10 and 100 to, and subtracting them from, 3-digit numbers
- Estimating answers to subtraction problems with 3-digit numbers
- Using the relationship of numbers in a subtraction expression to multiples of 100 to solve subtraction problems
- Solving addition problems with 3-digit numbers
- Estimating and solving addition problems with sums greater than 1,000
- Solving addition problems with more than 2 addends
- Estimating which of two sums is greater
- Knowing and using subtraction problems related to the addition combinations to $10 + 10$ (the subtraction facts, e.g., $8 - 5$, $13 - 9$) with fluency
- Determining combinations of addends for a given sum
- Solving addition and subtraction problems with more than one step
- Solving addition and subtraction problems in the context of money (dollars, cents)

Whole Number Operations **Understanding different types of subtraction problems**

Unit 3 Math Focus Points

- Solving subtraction problems that involve finding a missing part
- Visualizing and representing the action of a subtraction problem which involves finding a missing part
- Understanding comparison as the difference between two numbers
- Solving subtraction story problems that involve comparison
- Visualizing and representing the action of comparison problems
- Using number lines to represent solutions to comparison problems
- Solving subtraction problems that involve removal
- Visualizing and representing the action of removal problems

Whole Number Operations **Understanding the meaning of multiplication**

Unit 5 Math Focus Points

- Understanding multiplication as combining equal groups
- Writing and solving multiplication problems in contexts
- Identifying the number of groups, the number in each group, and the product in a multiplication situation
- Understanding the relationship among skip counting, repeated addition, and multiplication
- Using and understanding multiplication notation

Whole Number Operations **Reasoning about numbers and their factors and multiples**

Unit 5 Math Focus Points

- Finding the multiples of the numbers 2, 3, 4, 5, 6, and 10 by skip counting
- Describing and comparing characteristics of the multiples of a number
- Understanding that doubling (or halving) one factor in a multiplication expression doubles (or halves) the product

Whole Number Operations Understanding and working with an array model of multiplication

Unit 5 Math Focus Points

- Using arrays to model multiplication situations
- Using arrays to find factors of 2-digit numbers up to 50
- Using arrays to identify characteristics of numbers, including prime and square numbers
- Using arrays to find a product by skip counting by one of its dimensions
- Breaking an array into parts to find the product represented by the array

Computational Fluency Learning the multiplication combinations with products up to 50 fluently

Unit 5 Math Focus Points

- Using known multiplication combinations to determine the product of more difficult combinations
- Identifying and learning multiplication combinations not yet known fluently

Unit 8 Math Focus Points

- Fluently solving multiplication combinations with products to 50

Whole Number Operations Developing strategies for division based on understanding the inverse relationship between multiplication and division

Unit 5 Math Focus Points

- Understanding division as the splitting of a quantity into equal groups
- Using the inverse relationship between multiplication and division to solve problems
- Using multiplication combinations to solve division problems
- Using and understanding division notation
- Writing and solving division problems in contexts

Whole Number Operations Describing, analyzing, and comparing strategies for adding and subtracting whole numbers

Unit 8 Math Focus Points

- Using story contexts and representations to support explanations about how changing a number in a subtraction problem affects the difference (e.g., $200 - 75 = 125$ and $200 - 78 = 122$)
- Solving addition problems by changing the numbers to create an equivalent problem that is easier to solve
- Using story contexts and representations to support explanations about equivalent addition expressions (e.g., $88 + 105 = 90 + 103$)
- Identifying addition strategies by focusing on how each strategy starts
- Solving subtraction problems that involve comparison, removal, or finding missing part
- Subtracting 3-digit numbers by using strategies that involve either subtracting one number in parts, adding up, or subtracting back
- Representing solutions to subtraction problems with number lines, 1,000 charts, and/or story contexts
- Subtracting by using strategies that involve changing one number to make a problem that is easier to solve

Rational Numbers **Understanding the meaning of fractions (halves, fourths, eighths, thirds, sixths) and decimal fractions (0.50, 0.25) as equal parts of a whole (an object, an area, a set of objects)**

Unit 7 Math Focus Points

- Finding equal parts of a whole and naming them with fractions
- Dividing an area into equal parts
- Naming fractional parts with unit fractions ($\frac{1}{2}$, $\frac{1}{3}$, $\frac{1}{4}$, etc.)
- Ordering unit fractions
- Demonstrating that different-shaped pieces that are the same fraction of the same area have equal areas
- Naming fractional parts with fractions that have numerators greater than 1 ($\frac{3}{4}$, $\frac{2}{3}$, $\frac{3}{6}$, etc.)
- Dividing a group into equal parts and naming the parts with fractions
- Using fraction notation to record equivalencies (e.g., $\frac{3}{6} = \frac{1}{2}$, $\frac{1}{2} = \frac{2}{4}$)
- Identifying equivalent fractional parts
- Using mixed numbers to represent quantities greater than 1
- Identifying equivalent fractions and decimals for values involving halves and fourths (e.g., $\frac{1}{2} = 0.50$, $\frac{1}{4} = 0.25$, $2\frac{1}{2} = 2.5$)
- Reading, writing, and interpreting the meaning of the decimal numbers 0.50, 0.25, and numbers greater than 1 with these decimal portions, such as 2.5 and 2.25.

Rational Numbers **Using representations to combine fractions (halves, fourths, eighths, thirds, and sixths)**

Unit 7 Math Focus Points

- Using representations to combine fractions that sum to 1 (e.g., $\frac{1}{4} + \frac{3}{4} = 1$, $\frac{1}{3} + \frac{1}{3} + \frac{1}{3} = 1$, $\frac{1}{2} + \frac{1}{4} + \frac{1}{4} = 1$)
- Using representations to combine fractions to equal other fractions ($\frac{1}{2} = \frac{1}{3} + \frac{1}{6}$)

GRADE 3

Patterns, Functions, and Change

Using Tables and Graphs **Using graphs to represent change**

Unit 6 Math Focus Points

- Describing the overall shape of a line graph—increasing, decreasing, staying the same
- Finding the difference between values on a line graph, including the difference between a positive and negative value
- Associating a story with its corresponding graph
- Plotting points on a graph to represent a situation in which one quantity is changing in relation to another
- Identifying points on a graph with corresponding values in a table and interpreting the numerical information in terms of the situation the graph represents
- Comparing situations by describing differences in their graphs

Using Tables and Graphs **Using tables to represent change**

Unit 6 Math Focus Points

- Using tables to represent the relationship between two quantities in a situation with a constant rate of change
- Interpreting numbers in a table in terms of the situation they represent
- Comparing situations by describing differences in the tables that represent them

Linear Change Describing and representing a constant rate change

Unit 6 Math Focus Points

- Describing the relationship between two quantities in a situation with a constant rate of change, taking into account a beginning amount and a constant increase
- Creating a representation for a situation with a constant rate of change
- Comparing different representations that show the same situation
- Making rules that relate one variable to the other in situations with a constant rate of change
- Connecting the steps of a general method or rule to the parts of the situation they represent

Number Sequences Constructing, describing, and extending number sequences with constant increments generated by various contexts

Unit 6 Math Focus Points

- Identifying the unit of a repeating pattern
- Associating counting numbers with elements of a pattern
- Determining the element of an ABC pattern associated with a particular counting number
- Describing and extending a number sequence with a constant increment (e.g., 3, 6, 9, . . . or 2, 5, 8, . . .)
- Identifying numbers that are multiples of three, or one less or one more than a multiple of 3

GRADE 3

Data and Probability

Data Analysis Describing, summarizing, and comparing data

Unit 2 Math Focus Points

- Describing and interpreting categorical data
- Describing the shape of ordered, numerical data: where data are spread out or concentrated, where there are few data, highest and lowest values, and outliers
- Using summaries such as *almost all*, *very few*, *half*, or *more than half*
- Describing what values are typical or atypical in a data set
- Developing arguments based on the data
- Using data to compare groups

Data Analysis Representing data

Unit 2 Math Focus Points

- Developing classifications to organize categorical data
- Organizing categorical data in different ways to answer different questions
- Representing categorical data using a picture or graph
- Reading and interpreting a bar graph
- Reading a scale on a graph with intervals larger than 1
- Using a line plot, bar graph, or other representation to represent ordered, numerical data
- Interpreting what the numbers and symbols on a line plot mean
- Developing a consistent scale to show where data are and are not concentrated
- Reading and interpreting a representation of ordered, numerical data
- Considering how well a data representation communicates to an audience

Data Analysis Designing and carrying out a data investigation

Unit 2 Math Focus Points

- Developing and revising a survey question
- Interpreting results of a data investigation

GRADE 3

Geometry

Features of Shape Describing and classifying two-dimensional figures

Unit 4 Math Focus Points

- Determining the geometric moves needed (slides, flips, turns) to prove or disprove congruence between two shapes
- Identifying the attributes of triangles: three sides, three vertices, and three angles
- Identifying the attributes of quadrilaterals: four sides, four vertices, and four angles
- Comparing the properties of squares and rectangles

Features of Shape Describing and measuring angles

Unit 4 Math Focus Points

- Recognizing right angles
- Identifying a right angle as having a measure of 90 degrees
- Understanding angle size as the degree of turn
- Comparing the sizes of angles

Features of Shape Describing properties of three-dimensional shapes

Unit 9 Math Focus Points

- Describing the components and properties of different classes of solids such as polyhedra (3-D shapes having only flat surfaces, such as prisms and pyramids) and nonpolyhedra (such as cones and cylinders)
- Distinguishing between polyhedra and nonpolyhedra
- Distinguishing between prisms and pyramids
- Identifying the components of polyhedra (faces, edges, and vertices) and how they come together to form the whole
- Visualizing and building polyhedra by using knowledge of their components (faces, edges, and vertices) and how they come together to form the whole

Features of Shape Translating between two-dimensional and three-dimensional shapes

Unit 9 Math Focus Points

- Determining the number and shapes of the faces of cubes and other rectangular prisms and how they come together to form the whole
- Designing patterns that make open boxes for a cube
- Designing patterns that make open boxes for 2-cube rectangular prisms
- Designing patterns that make nets for triangular pyramids
- Determining the number and shapes of the faces of a triangular pyramid and how they come together to form the whole
- Communicating about spatial relationships
- Decomposing images of 3-D shapes and then recombining them to make a given structure

GRADE 3

Measurement

Linear Measurement **Measuring with standard units**

Unit 2 Math Focus Points

- Measuring in inches
- Measuring lengths longer than the measuring tool
- Understanding the relationship between feet and inches
- Combining feet and inches to get a total measurement
- Using correct notation to write a measurement in feet and inches

Unit 4 Math Focus Points

- Reviewing the length of units of measure (inch, foot, yard, centimeter, and meter)
- Establishing measurement benchmarks
- Using U.S. standard and metric units to accurately measure length
- Recognizing and explaining possible sources of measurement error

Linear Measurement **Understanding and finding perimeter**

Unit 4 Math Focus Points

- Understanding perimeter as the measure around the outside edges of a 2-dimensional figure
- Finding perimeter using standard units
- Creating different shapes with the same perimeter
- Finding the perimeter of an irregular shape

Area Measurement **Understanding and finding area**

Unit 4 Math Focus Points

- Understanding that area is measured in square units
- Understanding that when measuring area, the space being measured must be completely covered with no gaps or overlaps
- Using squares and triangles to make shapes with an area of four square units
- Examining the relationship between the area of squares and triangles
- Understanding that shapes with the same area can look different
- Finding the area of partially covered rectangles
- Finding the area of an irregular shape
- Designing a shape for a given area
- Finding area by counting or calculating whole and partial square units

Measuring Temperature **Understanding temperature and measuring with standard units**

Unit 6 Math Focus Points

- Reading and interpreting positive and negative temperatures on a thermometer and on a line graph
- Associating temperatures with particular activities or clothing

Volume **Structuring rectangular prisms and determining their volume**

Unit 9 Math Focus Points

- Determining the number of cubes that will fit in the box made by a given pattern
- Designing patterns for boxes that will hold a given number of cubes
- Seeing that the cubes filling a rectangular prism can be decomposed into congruent layers

GRADE 3

Classroom Routines

Class Collection

Unit 3 Math Focus Points

- Solving addition problems with 2- and 3-digit numbers
- Finding the difference between 3-digit numbers
- Finding the difference between 2- and 3-digit numbers and 1,000

What's the Temperature?

Units 1-9 Math Focus Points

- Learning about temperature: reading a thermometer, learning to associate different temperatures with words like *colder* and *warmer*, and establishing landmark temperatures
- Recording information in a table and on a graph
- Reading information from the shape of a graph: hot, cold, increasing, decreasing

Guess My Rule

Units 2, 6, and 8 Math Focus Points

- Using evidence and formulating questions to make hypotheses about the common characteristics of groups of people or things
- Systematically eliminating possibilities
- Using mathematical terms to describe numbers

More or Less?

Units 1, 2, and 9 Math Focus Points

- Breaking apart, reordering, or combining numbers within a problem, for easier computation
- Using knowledge of place value and known combinations to estimate sums and differences
- Practicing addition and subtraction skills

Practicing Place Value

Units 1 and 4 Math Focus Points

- Recognizing and interpreting the value of each digit in two- and three- digit numbers
- Finding different combinations of a number, using only 100s, 10s and 1s and recognizing their equivalence (e.g., 1 hundred, 3 tens and 7 ones = 1 hundred, 2 tens, and 17 ones = 13 tens and 7 ones = 12 tens and 17 ones, etc.)
- Reading and writing numbers up to 1,000
- Adding multiples of 10 to, and subtracting multiples of 10 from 2- and 3-digit numbers

GRADE 3

Ten-Minute Math

Counting Around the Class

Units 5 and 8 Math Focus Points

- Finding the multiples of numbers through skip counting
- Becoming familiar with multiplication patterns
- Understanding the relationship between skip counting and multiplication

Quick Images

Units 4 and 9 Math Focus Points

- Organizing and analyzing visual images
- Developing language and concepts needed to communicate about spatial relationships
- Decomposing images of 2-D shapes and then recombining them to make a given design (Unit 4)
- Decomposing images of 3-D shapes and then recombining them to make a given structure (Unit 9)

Today's Number

Units 2, 3, 6, and 7 Math Focus Points

- Generating equivalent expressions for a number using particular constraints
- Practicing computation skills
- Using notation to record expressions

What Time Is It?

Units 3, 5, and 7 Math Focus Points

- Naming, notating, and telling time to the nearest 5 minutes on a digital or analog clock
- Telling time to any minute on a digital or analog clock
- Determining intervals of time to the minute

GRADE 4

Number and Operations

Whole Number Operations Understanding and working with an array model of multiplication

Unit 1 Math Focus Points

- Using arrays to model multiplication situations
- Breaking an array into parts to find the product represented by the array
- Using arrays to find factors of 2-digit numbers
- Identifying features of numbers, including prime, square, and composite numbers

Whole Number Operations Reasoning about numbers and their factors

Unit 1 Math Focus Points

- Finding the multiples of a number by skip counting
- Determining whether one number is a factor or multiple of another
- Identifying the factors of a given number
- Identifying all the factors of 100
- Using knowledge of the factors of 100 to find factors of multiples of 100
- Using known multiplication combinations to find related multiplication combinations for a given product (e.g., if $4 \times 50 = 200$, then $8 \times 25 = 200$)
- Using representations to show that a factor of a number is also a factor of its multiples (e.g., if 25 is a factor of 100, then 25 is also a factor of 300)

Unit 3 Math Focus Points

- Understanding the effect of multiplying by a multiple of 10 (e.g., describing the relationship between 3×4 and 3×40)
- Finding multiples of 2-digit numbers

- Describing a sequence of multiples in order to predict other multiples
- Determining the effect on the product when a factor is doubled or halved

Whole Number Operations Understanding and using the relationship between multiplication and division to solve division problems

Unit 3 Math Focus Points

- Solving division story problems
- Using and interpreting division notation
- Solving division problems by making groups of the divisor
- Using known multiplication combinations to solve division problems

Unit 8 Math Focus Points

- Representing a multiplication or division problem with pictures or diagrams, including arrays and pictures of groups
- Using a story problem represented by a multiplication expression to keep track of parts of the problems

Whole Number Operations Describing, analyzing, and comparing strategies for adding and subtracting whole numbers

Unit 5 Math Focus Points

- Representing addition and subtraction on a number line
- Identifying, describing, and comparing addition and subtraction strategies by focusing on how each strategy starts
- Developing arguments about why two addition expressions are equivalent (e.g., $597 + 375 = 600 + 372$)
- Using story contexts and representations to support explanations about equivalent addition expressions
- Understanding the meaning of the steps and notation of the U.S. algorithm for addition
- Developing arguments about how the differences represented by two subtraction expressions are related (e.g., $432 - 198$ and $432 - 200$)
- Using story contexts and representations to support explanations about related subtraction expressions

Whole Number Operations Understanding different types of subtraction problems

Unit 5 Math Focus Points

- Understanding the action of subtraction problems
- Representing subtraction situations

Whole Number Operations Representing the meaning of multiplication and division

Unit 3 Math Focus Points

- Representing a multiplication or division problem with pictures, diagrams, or models
- Using arrays to model multiplication
- Making sense of remainders in terms of the problem context
- Creating a story problem to represent a division expression
- Comparing visual representations of multiplication situations

Whole Number Operations Understanding division as making groups of the divisor

Unit 8 Math Focus Points

- Solving division problems by breaking the problem into parts
- Using multiples of 10 to solve division problems
- Using the relationship between multiplication and division to solve division problems

The Base-Ten Number System **Extending knowledge of the number system to 10,000**

Unit 5 Math Focus Points

- Reading, writing, and sequencing numbers to 1,000 and 10,000
- Understanding the structure of 10,000 and its equivalence to one thousand 10s, one hundred 100s, and ten 1,000s
- Recognizing the place value of digits in large numbers

Computational Fluency **Fluency with multiplication combinations to 12×12**

Unit 1 Math Focus Points

- Identifying and learning multiplication combinations not yet known fluently
- Using known multiplication combinations to determine the products of more difficult combinations

Computational Fluency **Solving multiplication problems with 2-digit numbers**

Unit 3 Math Focus Points

- Developing strategies for multiplying that involve breaking apart numbers
- Reviewing multiplication combinations to 12×12
- Multiplying multiples of 10

Unit 8 Math Focus Points

- Estimating solutions to 2-digit multiplication problems
- Multiplying multiples of 10
- Solving 2-digit multiplication problems by breaking a problem into smaller parts and combining the subproducts
- Solving 2-digit multiplication problems by changing one factor to create an easier problem

Computational Fluency **Adding and subtracting accurately and efficiently**

Unit 5 Math Focus Points

- Adding and subtracting multiples of 10, 100, and 1,000
- Using multiples of 10 and 100 to find the difference between any 3-digit number and 1,000
- Adding 3- and 4-digit numbers
- Using clear and concise notation for recording addition and subtraction strategies
- Finding combinations of 3-digit numbers that add to 1,000
- Solving subtraction problems by breaking numbers apart
- Solving multistep addition and subtraction problems
- Combining positive and negative numbers

Rational Numbers **Understanding the meaning of fractions and decimal fractions**

Unit 6 Math Focus Points

- Finding fractional parts of a rectangular area
- Finding fractional parts of a group (of objects, people, etc.)
- Interpreting the meaning of the numerator and the denominator of a fraction
- Writing, reading, and applying fraction notation
- Representing fractions greater than 1
- Identifying everyday uses of fractions and decimals
- Reading and writing tenths and hundredths
- Representing tenths and hundredths as parts of an area

Rational Numbers **Comparing the values of fractions and decimal fractions**

Unit 6 Math Focus Points

- Identifying relationships between unit fractions when one denominator is a multiple of the other (e.g., halves and fourths, thirds and sixths)
- Comparing the same fractional parts of different-sized wholes
- Identifying equivalent fractions
- Ordering fractions and justifying their order through reasoning about fraction equivalencies and relationships
- Representing fractions using a number line
- Comparing fractions to the landmarks 0, $\frac{1}{2}$, 1, and 2
- Ordering decimals and justifying their order through reasoning about representations and meaning of the numbers
- Identifying decimal and fraction equivalents

Computation with Rational Numbers **Using representations to add rational numbers**

Unit 6 Math Focus Points

- Using representations to add fractions that sum to 1
- Estimating sums of fractions
- Adding fractions with the same and related denominators (e.g., halves, fourths, and eighths; thirds and sixths)
- Estimating sums of decimal numbers
- Adding decimal numbers that are multiples of 0.1 and 0.25 (e.g., 2.3 + 3.25)
- Using representations to combine tenths and hundredths

GRADE 4

Patterns, Functions, and Change

Using Tables and Graphs **Using graphs to represent change**

Unit 9 Math Focus Points

- Interpreting the points and shape of a graph in terms of the situation the graph represents
- Finding the difference between two values on a line graph
- Discriminating between features of a graph that represent quantity and those that represent changes in quantity
- Plotting points on a coordinate grid to represent a situation in which one quantity is changing in relation to another
- Identifying points in a graph with corresponding values in a table and interpreting the numerical information in terms of the situation the graph represents
- Comparing situations by describing differences in their graphs
- Describing the relative steepness of graphs or parts of graphs in terms of different rates of change
- Comparing tables, graphs, and situations of constant change with those of non-constant change

Using Tables and Graphs **Using tables to represent change**

Unit 9 Math Focus Points

- Interpreting numbers in a table in terms of the situation they represent
- Using tables to represent the relationship between two quantities in a situation of constant change

Linear Change Describing and representing a constant rate of change

Unit 9 Math Focus Points

- Describing the relationship between two quantities in a situation of constant change, taking into account a beginning amount and a constant increase
- Creating a representation for a situation of constant change
- Finding the value of one quantity in a situation of constant change, given the value of the other
- Writing an arithmetic expression for finding the value of one quantity in terms of the other in a situation of constant change
- Making rules that relate one variable to another in situations of constant change
- Using symbolic letter notation to represent the value of one variable in terms of another

GRADE 4

Data and Probability

Data Analysis Representing Data

Unit 2 Math Focus Points

- Organizing ordered numerical data to describe a data set
- Using a line plot to represent ordered numerical data
- Representing two sets of data in order to compare them

Data Analysis Describing, summarizing, and comparing data

Unit 2 Math Focus Points

- Describing the shape of a data set: where the data are spread out or concentrated, what the highest and lowest values are, what the range is, and what the outliers are
- Determining the range of a data set
- Describing and interpreting data that compare two groups
- Describing what values are typical or atypical in a data set
- Comparing two sets of data using the shape and spread of the data
- Finding the median of a data set
- Using medians to compare groups
- Considering what information a median does and does not provide

Data Analysis Analyzing and interpreting data

Unit 2 Math Focus Points

- Drawing conclusions based on data
- Developing arguments based on the data

Data Analysis Designing and carrying out a data investigation

Unit 2 Math Focus Points

- Recording and keeping track of data
- Considering how well a data representation communicates to an audience
- Developing and revising a survey question

Probability Describing the probability of an event

Unit 2 Math Focus Points

- Associating the word *probability* with the likelihood of an event
- Arranging events along a line representing the range of *certain* to *impossible*
- Associating verbal descriptions of probability with numeric descriptions
- Using numbers from 0 to 1 as measures of probability
- Comparing the expected probability of an event with the actual results of repeated trials of that event

GRADE 4

Geometry

Features of Shape Describing and classifying two-dimensional figures

Unit 4 Math Focus Points

- Defining polygons as closed figures with line segments as sides, and vertices
- Classifying polygons by attribute, including number of sides, length of sides, and size of angles
- Combining polygons to make new polygons
- Recognizing number of sides as a descriptor of various polygons
- Developing vocabulary to describe attributes and properties of quadrilaterals
- Understanding the relationship between squares and rectangles
- Making designs with mirror symmetry

Features of Shape Describing and measuring angles

Unit 4 Math Focus Points

- Identifying a right angle as 90 degrees
- Measuring acute angles by relating them to 90 degrees
- Using known angles to find the measure of other angles

Features of Shape Describing properties of three-dimensional shapes

Unit 7 Math Focus Points

- Describing attributes of geometric solids
- Naming geometric solids

Features of Shape Translating between two-dimensional and three-dimensional shapes

Unit 7 Math Focus Points

- Understanding how 3-D solids project silhouettes with 2-D shapes (for example, how a cone can produce both triangular and circular silhouettes)
- Decomposing images of 3-D shapes and then recombining them to make a given structure
- Visualizing what 3-D figures look like from different perspectives
- Recognizing how components of 3-D cube buildings come together to form the whole building
- Drawing silhouettes of 3-D cube buildings from different perspectives
- Integrating different silhouettes of an object, both to form a mental model and to build the whole object

GRADE 4

Measurement

Linear Measurement Measuring with standard units

Unit 2 Math Focus Points

- Using U.S. standard units to measure lengths longer than the measuring tool

Unit 4 Math Focus Points

- Reviewing the lengths of units of measure (inches, feet, yards, centimeters, meters)
- Using U.S. standard and metric units to accurately measure length
- Estimating lengths based on common units (centimeter, inch, foot, yard, meter)
- Determining when estimates or exact measurements are needed
- Finding perimeter using standard units

- Recognizing and explaining possible sources of measurement error
- Comparing different paths that have the same length

Unit 9 Math Focus Points

- Measuring in centimeters

Area Measurement Finding and understanding area

Unit 4 Math Focus Points

- Finding the area of symmetrical designs
- Understanding that the larger the unit of area, the smaller the number of units needed to measure the area
- Dividing irregular polygons into two shapes that have equal area
- Finding the area of polygons by decomposing shapes
- Finding the area of polygons using square units
- Finding the area of rectangles
- Finding the area of triangles in relation to the area of rectangles

Volume Structuring rectangular prisms and determining their volume

Unit 7 Math Focus Points

- Seeing that cubes filling a rectangular prism can be decomposed into congruent layers
- Finding the volume of cube buildings
- Designing patterns for boxes that hold a given number of cubes (volume)
- Developing a strategy for determining the volume of rectangular prisms
- Finding the number of cubes (volume) that will fit into the box made by a given pattern
- Doubling the number of cubes for a given box and considering how that changes the dimensions of the original box

GRADE 4

Ten-Minute Math

Closest Estimate

Units 8 and 9 Math Focus Points

- Approximating numbers to nearby landmark numbers, e.g. multiples of 10 or 100
- Calculating mentally
- Comparing answer choices to find the one closest to the actual answer

Counting Around the Class

Units 1, 3, and 8 Math Focus Points

- Finding the multiples of numbers through skip counting
- Becoming familiar with multiplication patterns
- Understanding the relationship between skip counting and multiplication

Practicing Place Value

Units 5, 6, and 7 Math Focus Points

- Reading and writing numbers up to 10,000
- Adding multiples of 10 to, and subtracting multiples of 10 from three- and four-digit numbers
- Reading and writing decimal fractions and decimal numbers
- Adding tenths and hundredths to, and subtracting them from decimal fractions and decimal numbers

Quick Images

Units 1, 4, and 7 Math Focus Points

- Organizing and analyzing visual images
- Developing language and concepts needed to communicate about spatial relationships
- Writing equations to represent the total number of dots in a pattern
- Decomposing images of 2-D shapes and then recombining them to make a given design (Unit 4)
- Decomposing images of 3-D shapes and then recombining them to make a given structure (Unit 7)

Quick Survey

Units 2, 6, and 9 Math Focus Points

- Describing features of the data
- Interpreting and posing questions about the data

Today's Number

Units 1, 2, 4, and 5 Math Focus Points

- Generating equivalent expressions for a number using particular constraints
- Practicing computation skills
- Using notation to record expressions

GRADE 5

Number and Operations

Whole Number Operations **Reasoning about numbers and their factors**

Unit 1 Math Focus Points

- Determining whether one number is a factor or multiple of another
- Identifying prime, square, even and odd numbers
- Using known multiplication combinations to find equivalent multiplication combinations (e.g., $18 = 3 \times 6 = 3 \times (2 \times 3)$)
- Using known multiplication combinations to find multiplication combinations for numbers related by place value (e.g., $3 \times 6 = 18$; $3 \times 6 \times 10 = 180$)
- Finding all the ways to multiply whole numbers for a given product
- Finding all the factors of a number
- Using properties (even, odd, prime, square) and relationships (factor, multiple) of numbers to solve problems
- Determining the prime factorization of a number

Computational Fluency **Solving multiplication problems with 2-digit numbers**

Unit 1 Math Focus Points

- Solving 2-digit by 2-digit multiplication problems
- Describing and comparing strategies used to solve multiplication problems
- Breaking up multiplication problems efficiently
- Multiplying fluently by multiples of 10
- Estimating the product of two numbers
- Comparing multiplication problems to determine which product is greater
- Identifying and learning multiplication combinations ("facts") not yet known fluently
- Using clear and concise notation

Whole Number Operations Understanding and using the relationship between multiplication and division to solve division problems

Unit 1 Math Focus Points

- Solving division problems with 2-digit divisors
- Using knowledge of multiples of 10 to solve division problems
- Using and interpreting notation that represents division and relating division and multiplication notations (e.g., $170 \div 15 =$ ___ and ___ $\times 15 = 170$)
- Describing and comparing strategies used to solve division problems
- Comparing division problems to determine which quotient is greater
- Solving a division problem by breaking the dividend into parts

Unit 3 Math Focus Points

- Solving division problems related to the multiplication combinations to 12×12 (the division "facts", e.g., $64 \div 8$, $54 \div 6$) with fluency

Whole Number Operations Representing the meaning of multiplication and division

Unit 1 Math Focus Points

- Writing multiplication equations that describe dot arrangements
- Using arrays to model multiplication
- Representing a multiplication or division problem with a picture or diagram
- Creating a story problem represented by a multiplication or division expression
- Making sense of remainders in terms of problem contexts

Unit 7 Math Focus Points

- Representing equivalent expressions in multiplication
- Representing equivalent expressions in division
- Representing a division problem with a picture or diagram
- Creating a story context for a division expression

Whole Number Operations Reasoning about equivalent expressions in multiplication and division

Unit 7 Math Focus Points

- Generating equivalent multiplication expressions by doubling (or tripling) one factor and dividing the other by 2 (or 3)
- Developing arguments about how to generate equivalent expressions in multiplication
- Using story contexts and representations to support explanations of the relationship between equivalent expressions
- Generating equivalent division expressions
- Comparing equivalent multiplication expressions to equivalent division expressions

Computational Fluency Solving multiplication problems with 2-digit and 3-digit numbers

Unit 7 Math Focus Points

- Describing and comparing strategies used to solve multidigit multiplication problems
- Solving 2-digit by 2-digit or 3-digit multiplication problems fluently
- Estimating answers to multiplication and division problems
- Understanding the U.S. algorithm for multiplication

Computational Fluency Solving division problems with 2-digit divisors

Unit 7 Math Focus Points

- Solving division problems with a 2-digit divisor fluently
- Describing and comparing strategies used to solve division problems

The Base-Ten Number System Extending knowledge of the number system to 100,000 and beyond

Unit 3 Math Focus Points

- Reading, writing, and sequencing numbers to 10,000 and 100,000
- Understanding the place-value relationships between 10, 100, 1,000, and 10,000
- Learning the names of places larger than 100,000: million, billion, trillion

Computational Fluency Adding and subtracting accurately and efficiently

Unit 3 Math Focus Points

- Adding and subtracting multiples of 100 and 1,000
- Finding the difference between a number and 10,000
- Finding combinations of 3-digit numbers that add to 1,000
- Solving addition and subtraction problems with large numbers by focusing on the place value of the digits
- Solving whole-number addition and subtraction problems efficiently
- Using clear and concise notation for recording addition and subtraction strategies
- Interpreting and solving multistep problems
- Using story contexts and representations, such as number lines, to explain and justify solutions to subtraction problems

Unit 7 Math Focus Points

- Using clear and concise notation
- Solving multistep word problems
- Using all four operations to solve problems

Whole Number Operations Examining and using strategies for subtracting whole numbers

Unit 3 Math Focus Points

- Identifying, describing, and comparing subtraction strategies by focusing on how each strategy starts
- Analyzing and using different subtraction strategies
- Developing arguments about how the differences represented by two subtraction expressions are related (e.g., 1,208 − 297 and 1,208 − 300)
- Understanding the meaning of the steps and notation of the U.S. algorithm for subtraction

Rational Numbers Understanding the meaning of fractions and percents

Unit 4 Math Focus Points

- Interpreting everyday uses of fractions, decimals, and percents
- Finding fractional parts of a whole or of a group (of objects, people, and so on)
- Finding fractional parts of a rectangular area
- Representing fractions on a number line
- Finding a percentage of a group (of objects, people, and so on)
- Finding a percentage of a rectangular area

- Identifying fraction and percent equivalents through reasoning about representations and known equivalents and relationships
- Interpreting the meaning of the numerator and denominator of a fraction
- Using equivalent fractions and percents to solve problems

Rational Numbers **Comparing fractions**

Unit 4 Math Focus Points

- Ordering fractions and justifying their order through reasoning about fraction equivalents and relationships
- Comparing fractions and percents to the landmarks 0, $\frac{1}{2}$, and 1
- Finding and comparing fractional parts and percents of a whole or a group
- Comparing fractional parts of different-sized wholes
- Using equivalencies to place fractions on a set of number lines (fraction tracks)
- Comparing fractions on a number line
- Ordering mixed numbers and fractions greater than 1

Rational Numbers **Understanding the meaning of decimal fractions**

Unit 6 Math Focus Points

- Identifying everyday uses of fractions and decimals
- Representing decimal fractions as parts of an area
- Reading and writing tenths, hundredths, and thousandths
- Identifying decimal, fraction, and percent equivalents
- Representing decimals using a number line
- Interpreting fractions as division
- Interpreting the meaning of digits in a decimal number

Rational Numbers **Comparing decimal fractions**

Unit 6 Math Focus Points

- Ordering decimals and justifying their order through reasoning about decimal representations, equivalents, and relationships
- Comparing decimals to the landmarks 0, $\frac{1}{2}$, and 1

Computation with Rational Numbers **Adding and subtracting fractions**

Unit 4 Math Focus Points

- Finding fractional parts of the rotation around a circle
- Adding fractions by using a rotation model
- Adding and subtracting fractions through reasoning about fraction equivalents and relationships
- Adding and subtracting fractions using a number line
- Finding combinations of fractions with sums between 0 and 2

Computation with Rational Numbers **Adding decimals**

Unit 6 Math Focus Points

- Estimating sums of decimal numbers
- Using representations to add tenths, hundredths, and thousandths
- Adding decimals to the thousandths through reasoning about place value, equivalents, and representations

GRADE 5

Patterns, Functions, and Change

Using Tables and Graphs **Using tables to represent change**

Unit 8 Math Focus Point

- Using tables to represent the relationship between two quantities

Using Tables and Graphs **Using graphs to represent change**

Unit 8 Math Focus Points

- Plotting points on a coordinate grid to represent a situation in which one quantity is changing in relation to another
- Identifying points in a graph with corresponding values in a table and interpreting the numerical information in terms of the situation the graph represents
- Describing the relative steepness of graphs or parts of graphs in terms of different rates of change
- Comparing situations by describing differences in their graphs

Linear Change **Describing and representing situations with a constant rate of change**

Unit 8 Math Focus Points

- Describing the relationship between two quantities in a situation with a constant rate of change, taking into account a beginning amount and a constant increase (or decrease)
- Finding the value of one quantity in a situation with a constant rate of change, given the value of the other (e.g., if you know the age, what is the height? or if you know the number of rows, what is the perimeter?)
- Writing an arithmetic expression for finding the value of one quantity in terms of the other in a situation with a constant rate of change
- Making rules that relate one variable to the other in situations with a constant rate of change
- Using symbolic letter notation to represent the value of one variable in terms of another variable

Nonlinear Change **Describing and representing situations in which the change is not constant**

Unit 8 Math Focus Points

- Comparing tables, graphs, and situations with a constant rate of change with those in which the rate of change is not constant
- Describing a situation in which the rate of change is not constant but can be determined
- Describing how a graph represents a situation in which the rate of change is not constant

GRADE 5

Data and Probability

Data Analysis **Representing data**

Unit 9 Math Focus Points

- Using a line plot to represent ordered, numerical data
- Representing two sets of data in order to compare them
- Considering how well a data representation communicates to an audience

Data Analysis **Describing, summarizing, and comparing data**

Unit 9 Math Focus Points

- Comparing sets of data using the shape and spread of the data

- Describing the shape of a set of data: where the data are concentrated, the median, what is typical, highest and lowest values, range and outliers
- Using medians to compare groups

Data Analysis **Analyzing and interpreting data**

Unit 9 Math Focus Points

- Developing arguments based on data
- Drawing conclusions based on data
- Considering how well conclusions are supported by data

Data Analysis **Designing and carrying out a data investigation**

Unit 9 Math Focus Points

- Designing an experiment to answer a question about two groups, objects, or conditions
- Developing and carrying out consistent procedures for collecting data from an experiment
- Recording and keeping track of a set of data
- Carrying out multiple trials in an experiment

Probability **Describing the probability of an event**

Unit 9 Math Focus Points

- Comparing the expected probability of an event with the actual results of repeated trials of that event
- Using numbers from 0 to 1 as measures of probability
- Determining the fairness of a game based on the probability of winning for each player

GRADE 5

Geometry

Features of Shape **Translating between two-dimensional and three-dimensional shapes**

Unit 2 Math Focus Point

- Decomposing 3-D shapes and then recombining them to make a given building

Features of Shape **Describing and classifying two-dimensional figures**

Unit 5 Math Focus Points

- Identifying attributes of polygons
- Describing triangles by the sizes of their angles and the lengths of their sides
- Using attributes to describe and compare quadrilaterals including parallelograms, rectangles, rhombuses, and squares
- Defining a regular polygon as a polygon with all sides and all angles equal

Features of Shape **Describing and measuring angles**

Unit 5 Math Focus Point

- Using known angles to find the measures of other angles

Features of Shape **Creating and describing similar shapes**

Unit 5 Math Focus Points

- Recognizing and building similar figures
- Examining the relationship among angles, line lengths, and areas of similar polygons
- Making a generalization about the changes in area of similar figures

- Building similar figures for polygons made from two or more Power Polygon pieces
- Using Power Polygons to find the areas of similar hexagons

GRADE 5

Measurement

Linear and Area Measurement **Finding perimeter and area of rectangles**

Unit 5 Math Focus Points

- Comparing the perimeters and areas of rectangles when the dimensions are multiplied by given amounts
- Using numerical and/or geometric patterns to describe how the perimeters and areas of rectangles change when the dimensions change
- Using representations to explain how perimeters and areas of rectangles change
- Creating different rectangles with the same area but different perimeters
- Understanding square units as a unit of measure
- Creating different rectangles with the same perimeter but different areas
- Describing the shapes of rectangles that have the same area or the same perimeter

Unit 8 Math Focus Points

- Measuring length with meters and centimeters
- Finding the perimeter of a rectangle
- Finding the area of a rectangle

Volume **Structuring rectangular prisms and determining their volume**

Unit 2 Math Focus Points

- Determining the number of cubes that will fit into the box made by a given pattern
- Developing a strategy for determining the volume of rectangular prisms
- Designing patterns for boxes that hold a given number of cubes
- Finding the volume of rectangular prisms
- Considering how the dimensions of a box change when the volume is changed (doubled, halved, or tripled)
- Organizing rectangular packages to fit in rectangular boxes
- Designing a box that can be completely filled with several differently-shaped rectangular packages
- Determining the volume, in cubic centimeters, of a small prism
- Constructing units of volume—cubic centimeter, cubic inch, cubic foot, cubic yard (optional), cubic meter
- Choosing an appropriate unit of volume to measure a large space
- Finding the volume of a large space, such as the classroom, using cubic meters
- Describing and defending measurement methods

Volume **Structuring prisms, pyramids, cylinders, and cones and determining their volume**

Unit 2 Math Focus Points

- Comparing volumes of differently-shaped containers
- Building rectangular solids
- Finding volume relationships between solids, particularly those with the same base and height
- Building a prism with three times the volume of a given pyramid
- Demonstrating the 3:1 relationship between rectangular prisms and pyramids with the same base and height
- Finding volume, in cubic centimeters, of prisms, pyramids, cylinders, and cones

Ten-Minute Math

Estimation and Number Sense

Units 2-4 and 6-9 Math Focus Points

- Estimating solutions to 2- and 3-digit multiplication and division problems
- Estimating solutions to 4- and 5-digit addition and subtraction problems
- Breaking apart, reordering, or changing numbers mentally to determine a reasonable estimate

Guess My Rule

Unit 4 Math Focus Points

- Identifying fractions of a group
- Using evidence and formulating questions to make hypotheses about the common characteristics of groups of people
- Systematically eliminating possibilities

Number Puzzles

Units 1 and 7 Math Focus Points

- Identifying prime, square, even, and odd numbers
- Determining if one number is a factor or multiple of another

Practicing Place Value

Units 3, 8, and 6 Math Focus Points

- Recognizing and interpreting the value of each digit in 4- and 5-digit numbers
- Finding different combinations of a number, using only 1,000s, 100s, 10s, and 1s and recognizing their equivalency (i.e. 1 hundred, 3 tens, and 7 ones = 12 tens and 17 ones, etc.)
- Reading and writing numbers up to 100,000
- Adding multiples of 10 to, and subtracting multiples of 10 from 4- and 5-digit numbers
- Reading and writing decimal fractions and decimal numbers
- Adding tenths or hundredths to, and subtracting them from, decimal fractions and decimal numbers

Quick Images

Units 1, 2, and 5 Math Focus Points

- Organizing and analyzing visual images
- Developing language and concepts needed to communicate about spatial relationships
- Writing multiplication and division equations to represent the total number of shapes in a pattern
- Decomposing images of 2-D shapes and then recombining them to make a given design (Unit 5)
- Decomposing images of 3-D shapes and then recombining them to make a given structure (Unit 2)

Quick Survey

Units 5 and 9 Math Focus Points

- Describing features of the data
- Interpreting and posing questions about the data

NCTM Curriculum Focal Points and Connections

The set of three curriculum focal points and related connections for mathematics in grade 4 follow. These topics are the recommended content emphases for this grade level. It is essential that these focal points be addressed in contexts that promote problem solving, reasoning, communication, making connections, and designing and analyzing representations.

Grade 4 Curriculum Focal Points	*Investigations* Units
***Number and Operations* and *Algebra:* Developing quick recall of multiplication facts and related division facts and fluency with whole number multiplication** Students use understandings of multiplication to develop quick recall of the basic multiplication facts and related division facts. They apply their understanding of models for multiplication (i.e., equal-sized groups, arrays, area models, equal intervals on the number line), place value, and properties of operations (in particular, the distributive property) as they develop, discuss, and use efficient, accurate, and generalizable methods to multiply multidigit whole numbers. They select appropriate methods and apply them accurately to estimate products or calculate them mentally, depending on the context and numbers involved. They develop fluency with efficient procedures, including the standard algorithm, for multiplying whole numbers, understand why the procedures work (on the basis of place value and properties of operations), and use them to solve problems.	**Addressed in the work of:** • *Factors, Multiples, and Arrays* (Multiplication and Division 1) • *Multiple Towers and Division Stories* (Multiplication and Division 2) • *How Many Packages? How Many Groups?* (Multiplication and Division 3) • Ten-Minute Math: *Closest Estimate, Counting Around the Class, Quick Images: Seeing Numbers, Today's Number* **Also supported in the work of:** • *Penny Jars and Plant Growth* (Patterns, Functions, and Change) • *Moving Between Solids and Silhouettes* (3-D Geometry and Measurement)
***Number and Operations:* Developing an understanding of decimals, including the connections between fractions and decimals** Students understand decimal notation as an extension of the base-ten system of writing whole numbers that is useful for representing more numbers, including numbers between 0 and 1, between 1 and 2, and so on. Students relate their understanding of fractions to reading and writing decimals that are greater than or less than 1, identifying equivalent decimals, comparing and ordering decimals, and estimating decimal or fractional amounts in problem solving. They connect equivalent fractions and decimals by comparing models to symbols and locating equivalent symbols on the number line.	**Addressed in the work of:** • *Fraction Cards and Decimal Squares* (Fractions and Decimals) • Ten-Minute Math: *Practicing Place Value* **Also supported in the work of:** • *Describing the Shape of the Data* (Data Analysis and Probability)
***Measurement:* Developing an understanding of area and determining the areas of two-dimensional shapes** Students recognize area as an attribute of two-dimensional regions. They learn that they can quantify area by finding the total number of same-sized units of area that cover the shape without gaps or overlaps. They understand that a square that is 1 unit on a side is the standard unit for measuring area. They select appropriate units, strategies (e.g., decomposing shapes), and tools for solving problems that involve estimating or measuring area. Students connect area measurements to the area model that they have used to represent multiplication, and they use this connection to justify the formula for the area of a rectangle.	**Addressed in the work of:** • *Size, Shape, and Symmetry* (2-D Geometry and Measurement) • Ten-Minute Math: *Quick Images-2D* **Also supported in the work of:** • *Factors, Multiples, and Arrays* (Multiplication and Division 1) • Technology: *LogoPaths* Software

Connections to the Focal Points	*Investigations* Units
Algebra: Students continue identifying, describing, and extending numeric patterns involving all operations and nonnumeric growing or repeating patterns. Through these experiences, they develop an understanding of the use of a rule to describe a sequence of numbers or objects.	**Addressed in the work of:** • *Penny Jars and Plant Growth* (Patterns, Functions, and Change) • Ten-Minute Math: *Today's Number* **Also supported in the work of:** • *Factors, Multiples, and Arrays* (Multiplication and Division 1)
Geometry: Students extend their understanding of properties of two-dimensional shapes as they find the areas of polygons. They build on their earlier work with symmetry and congruence in grade 3 to encompass transformations, including those that produce line and rotational symmetry. By using transformations to design and analyze simple tilings and tessellations, students deepen their understanding of two-dimensional space.	**Addressed in the work of:** • *Size, Shape, and Symmetry* (2-D Geometry and Measurement) • Ten-Minute Math: *Quick Images-2D* • Technology: *LogoPaths Software* **Also supported in the work of:** • *Moving Between Solids and Silhouettes* (3-D Geometry and Measurement) • *Factors, Multiples, and Arrays* (Multiplication and Division 1) • *Multiple Towers and Division Stories* (Multiplication and Division 2)
Measurement: As part of understanding two-dimensional shapes, students measure and classify angles.	**Addressed in the work of:** • *Size, Shape, and Symmetry* (2-D Geometry and Measurement) • Technology: *LogoPaths* Software
Data Analysis: Students continue to use tools from grade 3, solving problems by making frequency tables, bar graphs, picture graphs, and line plots. They apply their understanding of place value to develop and use stem-and-leaf plots.	**Addressed in the work of:** • *Describing the Shape of the Data* (Data Analysis and Probability) • Ten-Minute Math: *Quick Survey*
Number and Operations: Building on their work in grade 3, students extend their understanding of place value and ways of representing numbers to 100,000 in various contexts. They use estimation in determining the relative sizes of amounts or distances. Students develop understandings of strategies for multidigit division by using models that represent division as the inverse of multiplication, as partitioning, or as successive subtraction. By working with decimals, students extend their ability to recognize equivalent fractions. Students' earlier work in grade 3 with models of fractions and multiplication and division facts supports their understanding of techniques for generating equivalent fractions and simplifying fractions.	**Addressed in the work of:** • *Landmarks and Large Numbers* (Addition, Subtraction, and the Number System) • *Factors, Multiples, and Arrays* (Multiplication and Division 1) • *Multiple Towers and Division Stories* (Multiplication and Division 2) • *How Many Packages? How Many Groups?* (Multiplication and Division 3) • *Fraction Cards and Decimal Squares* (Fractions and Decimals) • Ten-Minute Math: *Closest Estimate, Counting Around the Class, Practicing Place Value, Quick Images: Seeing Numbers, Today's Number*

PART 9

Grade 4 Math Terms and Index

Each entry is identified by the Curriculum Unit number (in yellow) and its page number(s).

Grade 4 Curriculum Units

U1 Factors, Multiples and Arrays
U2 Describing the Shape of the Data
U3 Multiple Towers and Division Stories
U4 Size, Shape, and Symmetry
U5 Landmarks and Large Numbers
U6 Fraction Cards and Decimal Squares
U7 Moving Between Solids and Silhouettes
U8 How Many Packages? How Many Groups?
U9 Penny Jars and Plant Growth

A

B

C

D

E

F

G

H

I

J

K

L

M

Grade 4 Curriculum Units

U1 Factors, Multiples and Arrays
U2 Describing the Shape of the Data
U3 Multiple Towers and Division Stories
U4 Size, Shape, and Symmetry
U5 Landmarks and Large Numbers
U6 Fraction Cards and Decimal Squares
U7 Moving Between Solids and Silhouettes
U8 How Many Packages? How Many Groups?
U9 Penny Jars and Plant Growth

N

O

P

Q

R

S

T

Grade 4 Curriculum Units

- U1 Factors, Multiples and Arrays
- U2 Describing the Shape of the Data
- U3 Multiple Towers and Division Stories
- U4 Size, Shape, and Symmetry
- U5 Landmarks and Large Numbers
- U6 Fraction Cards and Decimal Squares
- U7 Moving Between Solids and Silhouettes
- U8 How Many Packages? How Many Groups?
- U9 Penny Jars and Plant Growth